COOL MAGIC TRICKS

COOL MAGIC TRICKS

Although most of us can't explain how a microchip powers our computer or remember the principles of electricity once our science lesson is over, we readily accept what these and other marvels of technology can do for us. But who hasn't looked on in awe as a smiling magician makes a coin disappear and reappear seemingly at will? We love mysteries and that's the appeal of magic.

To help you put on the best magic show possible, we've put together some tips. Follow these and you're sure to astonish your family and friends.

1 Never tell anyone how a trick is done.

2 Practice each trick, story, and patter in your repertoire until you know it perfectly and can do it over and over without a mistake.

3 Don't repeat a trick in front of the same audience.

4 Use expressions and gestures to enhance your act: frown to show you're concentrating hard, stand quietly to gain your audience's attention, or use sweeping arm gestures to call upon your 'magical powers'.

5 Finally, and most importantly, have fun!

Contents

You need: a pencil, a piece of paper, a calculator (optional)

This mind-reading trick uses the 'magical' number nine. Performed with the help of a friend, this trick will greatly enhance your act and impress your audience!

1 Tell your friend to write down any three-digit number he likes, but the digits must decrease in value, such as 9, 7 and 2. He must not let you see what he's written.

2 Then tell your friend to write the same number backwards underneath the first—that would be 2, 7 and 9.

3 Now he must subtract this number from the first and tell you only the final digit. In our example, this is 3.

4 You will immediately be able to tell him that the remaining numbers are 6 and 9, because you will subtract the 3 from the 9 to find the first digit—that will be 6. The middle digit is always 9, no matter what three-digit number your friend chose! There's that sneaky 9 again!

Fun Facts
There are 2 types of magic. The first refers to supernatural, mystical, and paranormal practices. The second is the art of entertaining audiences by performing illusions and tricks—this is the kind you're learning now!

More Mind-reading

You need: a pencil, a piece of paper, a calculator

Tricks that involve mind-reading and numbers are always fascinating—here's another easy and effective one to include in your show.

1 Ask a friend to write down a number. It can be any number she likes (it doesn't matter how many digits) provided the digits do not decrease in value. Your friend should not show you the number until the end of the trick.

2 Ask your friend to multiply the number she wrote down by 10. (Let's pretend your friend chose the number 15689.)

$$15689 \times 10 = 156890$$

3 Ask your friend to subtract the first number from the second number.

$$156890 - 15689 = 141201$$

4 Ask your friend to add 9 to the answer.

$$141201 + 9 = 141210$$

5 Ask your friend to cross out any number except a zero and tell you what the remaining digits are. In our example, the second 1 is crossed out and the remaining numbers are 1, 4, 2, 1 and 0.

141210

6 You add these remaining digits in your head—they come to 8—and then subtract the total from 9 to find out what number was crossed out.

7 Tell your friend the number she crossed out was 1! Mind-reading wins again!

Trick
3

You need: a paper strip about 30 cm (12 in.) by 4 cm (1.5 in.), glue, scissors

This quick little illusion will have your audience believing you can do anything!

1 Hold the paper strip and twist it once.

2 Then glue the ends together.

3 Cut around the center of the ring carefully. What's the result? Two rings? No, it's one big ring if you've cut correctly.

4 Now to take this a little further—cut around the center again. Do you think you'll get a really big ring this time? No! This time there are two rings!

Quick Tricks and Simple Illusions

Something Goes!

You need: a coin, a blunt pencil

Tell your audience you can make a coin disappear—but it seems you need more practice!

1 Stand with your left side towards your audience if you are right-handed or your right side toward them if you are left-handed. Put the coin in the hand closest to the audience and hold it up, explaining that it will disappear once you tap it sharply three times with your pencil.

2 Hold the end of the pencil with the fingers of your other hand and bring it up into the air until it is level with your ear.

3 Bring the pencil down and tap the coin sharply with it while exclaiming a really loud 'One.'

ONE!

4 Do this again—bringing the pencil up to exactly the same height and down again, tapping the coin and saying 'Two.'

5 Without missing a beat, bring the pencil up one more time, this time sliding it easily and quickly behind your ear. Bring your now-empty hand down, saying 'Three!', and look really surprised to discover the pencil has vanished.

THREE!

6 Turn away from the audience, without showing the pencil if possible, and mutter something about having to go and practice the trick more.

7 Remember—to succeed with this trick you need to keep the same 'beat' going when counting. Don't pause between any of the taps of the coin, especially not before the third tap!

Hey... I'm not a happy Pharoah...!
What happened to the Vanishing Pyramid Trick and turning a camel into a palm tree?

Did you know?
The first record of performing magicians is in the Westcar Papyrus in the State Museum of Berlin, Germany. It contains documented proof that magicians performed for the Pharaohs of ancient Egypt about 4500 years ago.

> **You need:** a deck of cards, a calculator, a piece of paper, a pencil

Using your magical powers, you are able to name the card hidden in an assistant's pocket.

1 Ask a volunteer to come forward and write down any four-digit number on a piece of paper, without letting you see any of the numbers. The only condition is the four numbers must be different. (In our example, we'll use the number 7539.)

2 Ask him to add the four numbers together and write down the total. Now give him the calculator and ask him to subtract the total from the original number.

3 Hand the volunteer a deck of cards and ask him to secretly remove four cards which have the same numbers as the four digits (an ace = 1 and a king = 0). Each card must be a different suit.

4 Ask your volunteer to put one card (which isn't a king) in his pocket, or out of sight, and hand you the other three cards. In our example, the volunteer puts the five of clubs in his pocket.

5 Now you must mentally add the values of the three cards. If the answer has more than one digit, add those digits until there is only one digit. (For example, 13 becomes 1 + 3 = 4).

6 Mentally subtract this number from 9, and the value of the card in your volunteer's pocket will appear, as if by magic! It's a five—and because you are holding cards that are hearts, spades, and diamonds—the card must be the five of clubs!

7 The only exception to this clever little trick is when you mentally subtract the value of the cards from 9 and the answer is 0—the missing card isn't a king, it's a 9.

that's amazing!

Diabolically Clever Card Tricks

Who's Lying?

You need: a deck of cards, a table

Card tricks are a magician's stock in trade. Everyone expects you to be able to flip, shuffle, twist, and 'read' cards telepathically—so let's get on with it!

1 Before your audience arrives, shuffle the deck of cards—make sure you know which card is on the bottom.

2 Once your audience is seated, fan out the deck of cards on the table in front of you and ask a volunteer to choose one card. She is not to show or tell you its identity.

3 While the volunteer looks at the card, you should close the fan of cards, straighten the deck, and place it on the table, face-down. Ask the volunteer to cut the deck into two equal piles.

4 Now ask your volunteer to put her card on the pile she cut from the top of the deck, then place the other half of the deck on top of this. This should mean the card you memorized, which was at the bottom of the pile a minute ago, is now on top of the selected card.

5 Now is the time for some good magician's patter. Explain to the audience the deck of cards is special—it can detect lies!

6 Explain to your volunteer that you are going to turn each card over and ask her if this is the card she selected. She is to say 'No' every time, even when you turn over her selected card. The deck of cards will 'tell' you when she is lying. Obviously you are looking for the card you memorized—the card after it will be the selected card.

7 When you turn over the selected card and your volunteer says 'No,' yell 'Liar!' loudly and watch her reaction!

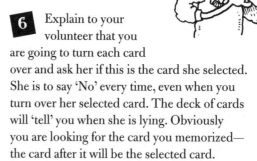

My magic pack of cards tells me you might be telling fibbies!

You need: a deck of cards, a table, a wand (optional)

Make a magician out of a volunteer with this trick. Your volunteer will pick a card, place it back in the deck, wave a magic wand—and hey presto!—the card will have magically turned over in the deck!

1 Before the audience arrives, turn over the bottom card in the deck so the deck looks the same from both ends.

2 From your audience, select a volunteer, then spread the cards face-down on the table— taking care not to show the reversed card on the bottom of the pack. Ask your volunteer to select a card and show it to the audience, but not to you.

3 As the volunteer is showing the card to the audience, you should close the deck in the palm of one hand and secretly turn it over so that the reversed bottom card is now on top of the deck. You need to practice this movement to make it so smooth that no one will notice you doing it.

4 Ask your volunteer to place the card face-down anywhere she likes in the deck that you are still holding. What she's done of course is place the selected card backwards in the deck of cards.

5 Now tell the volunteer she is going to perform the magic trick with the help of your magic wand (if you have one) or by speaking some magic words that you will tell her. Turn over the hand holding the deck, so it is now palm down, and put the deck of cards flat on the table. Now the deck is right-side up again with the reversed card on the bottom of the pack. The selected card is also reversed.

Now…say…SIM SALA BIM and let's hope it doesn't turn into a toad!

6 Once your volunteer has woven her magic spell over the cards, you can pick up the deck and spread the cards in a fan on the table or move them from hand to hand until you come to the selected card, which of course will be reversed face-up within the deck. Show the audience the card. Congratulate your new assistant and take the applause with her!

ONE DAY…MAGICIANS WILL PULL RABBITS OUT OF HATS AND GET PAID FOR IT!

Did you know?
In England, in the early 1700s, magic was considered respectable entertainment. Magicians performed in private homes, at booths at village fairs, and in theaters.

Diabolically Clever Card Tricks

Arise Card

Trick

8

You need: a deck of cards

Make any card you name rise out of the deck.

1 Ask a volunteer to shuffle the deck of cards.

2 When the deck is handed back to you, straighten it, taking note of which card is face-down on top. Perhaps it is the ten of diamonds.

3 Hold the deck vertically in one hand (left if you are right-handed and right if you are left-handed), so the cards are facing the audience.

4 Place your other hand behind the deck and rest your forefinger or index finger on top of the deck. Now extend your little finger (or ring finger if it is easier) until it touches the back of the top card (the ten of diamonds).

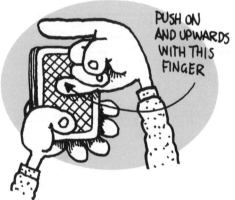

PUSH ON AND UPWARDS WITH THIS FINGER

5 Now all you need to do is name the card and ask it to rise for you! 'Ten of diamonds...arise now from your slumber!' While you are saying this, push upward on the top card with your little or ring finger. Do it slowly, making sure your forefinger or index finger is rising as you speak. From where the audience is sitting, it will look as if your forefinger or index finger is encouraging the rising card to rise, and it will also look as if the card is coming from the middle of the deck. Easy but effective!

You need: a deck of cards, a table, good mathematics skills!

At first, this trick may seem hard to understand. It's best to practice the trick while reading the instructions.

1 Place the cards on the table and ask a volunteer to remove a small bunch of them. Watch and try to estimate how many cards he takes.

2 You now take a bunch of cards yourself. Make sure it's more than your volunteer took.

3 Ask your volunteer to count his cards while you turn your back. He must count silently. While your back is turned you also count your cards silently and accurately.

4 Perhaps you have 16 cards. Now you need to use your math skills. Subtract any number from 1 to 5 from your total. Say you subtract 4, your new total is 12.

5 What you now say to your volunteer is: 'I bet I have as many cards as you, plus 4 extra (the number between 1 and 5 you chose), and enough left over to make yours equal 12 (your new total).'

6 The volunteer tells you how many cards he has and you deal this exact number from your pile. So if your volunteer has 10 cards, you deal 10 cards. You now say: 'That's the number of cards you had.' Deal 4 more cards, counting out loud, and say 'That's the four extra', and finally deal out what's left in your hand. In our example, it should be 2 cards. These 2 cards plus the number of cards your volunteer had in the beginning add up to 12.

7 It sounds complicated, but the more you practice the trick on your own, the easier it will become and you'll find it works every time!

Your Card Is

Trick 10

You need: a deck of cards

Another simple but effective trick to show you are a master or mistress of the cards! Yet again, you will find the 'selected' card hidden in the deck. Remember to deal the cards the same way every time.

1 Deal out three piles with seven cards in each pile, laying them out one, one, one, and two, two, two, rather than dealing one pile at a time. Put the remainder of the deck to one side—it won't be needed.

2 Ask an audience member to pick a card from any pile and to remember it, but not tell anyone what it is. He should then put the card back in the same pile.

3 You now gather up the three piles of cards, making sure the pile with the selected card is between the other two piles, then deal them out again, into three groups of seven cards.

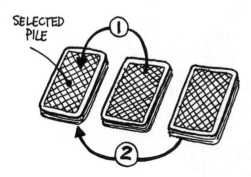

SELECTED PILE

4 Ask your volunteer to inspect each pile of cards and tell you which pile the selected card is now in.

5 Again gather all the piles of cards, keeping the selected card's pile in the middle of the other two piles, and deal them out into three groups of seven.

6 The volunteer again finds his selected card and indicates to you which pile it is now in. You gather the piles up, again keeping the selected card's pile in the middle of the other two.

7 Spell out Y-O-U-R-C-A-R-D-I-S by removing a card for each letter and the next card will be the selected card!

Yes... don't worry... I even amaze myself!

You need: a deck of cards, a ring, a toothpick, a table

This is another easy trick for young (and old!) magicians. It's easy to learn, easy to perform, and easy to make look good!

1 To get ready for this trick, put on the ring. Now turn your palm so it's facing up. Slide the toothpick into the ring.

2 Place your hand carefully down on the table, making sure the audience doesn't see the toothpick. Your patter needs to include telling the audience you are about to magically lift several playing cards with just the palm of your hand. You won't be holding on to them; they will just magically rise as you lift your hand.

3 Take a card with your other hand and slide it under the hand on the table, making sure one end of the card slides under the toothpick.

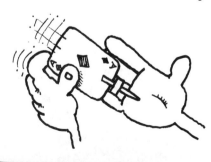

4 Pick up another card and slide it under your hand from the other direction. This time you want it between your hand and the other end of the toothpick.

5 Try putting another four cards under your hand now. They will be held in place by the original two cards.

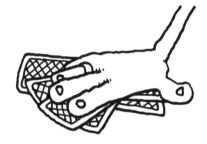

6 Say your favorite magic phrase, such as 'Abracadabra' or 'Sim sala bim', and slowly lift your hand with the cards horizontally above the table. The cards will stay with your hand—it's magic!

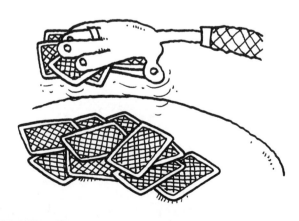

Gone! Into Thin Air

Trick

12

You need: a deck of cards, a handkerchief with a hem, a toothpick, scissors, a table

So you've dazzled the audience by finding the cards they've picked, but how about making cards disappear? That would be fun…

1 A little bit of preparation for this trick is necessary. Make sure the toothpick is as long as the width of a playing card—if it's too long, trim it. Now poke this toothpick into the hem of the handkerchief. You're ready for an audience!

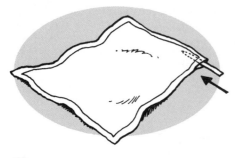

2 Begin with a flourish by spreading the deck of cards on the table. Wave the handkerchief about and tell your audience you'll pick a card from the deck and make it vanish into thin air.

3 Lay the handkerchief over the cards so the edge with the toothpick is folded under the handkerchief.

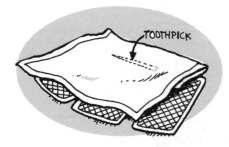

TOOTHPICK

4 Pick up the edge of the handkerchief which contains the toothpick by holding the toothpick between your thumb and index finger—it looks as if you are holding a card, right?

5 Say your favorite magic words, including something about making the card disappear. Throw the handkerchief into the air—the card appears to have vanished!

TRUE MAGIC! Look at that! NO CARD!

The Coin Fold

Another easy but effective trick using just one coin—especially suitable for a small audience.

1 Place the coin in the center of the piece of paper.

2 Fold the bottom edge of the paper up and over the coin, leaving a 6 mm (0.25 in.) gap between the two edges of the paper.

3 Fold the right edge of the paper back behind the coin.

4 Then fold the left edge of the paper back behind the coin.

5 Make the final fold by bending the top flap of the paper back behind the coin. It seems as if the coin is completely wrapped, but in fact the top edge is still open.

6 You now turn the package around so the open edge allows the coin to slip into the palm of your hand, where it stays while you 'prove' the coin has disappeared by tearing up the paper package.

Did you know?
Harry Houdini (Ehrich Weiss was his real name) is still the best known magician. He was known as an escapologist, and his catchcry was 'No Jail Could Hold Him!' He often performed outdoors too, which added to the drama. He escaped from a straightjacket while hanging by his ankles tied high above a street—he received plenty of publicity for that trick!

Cunning Coin Conundrums

Sleight of Hand

You need: one coin

All magicians learn sleight of hand. Learn this trick well and you can perform it at any time in any place—a show, a party, or even a restaurant!

1 Begin by placing the coin firmly between the index and middle fingers of one hand. The coin should be hidden, so that when you present your open hand (palm out) to the audience they can't see a thing.

> **Did you know?**
> By the 1800s, magic was often performed in theaters in many countries. At some venues, magicians performed regularly.

From the other side... Can't see the coin

2 Now we come to the part that you need to practice and practice. To produce the coin, you turn your fingers in towards the palm of your hand and use your thumb to bring the coin to the front.

The Weeping Coin

You need: a coin, a small piece of wet (but not dripping) sponge

An emotional, crying coin? Whatever next!

1 Before your audience arrives, wet the piece of sponge and make sure it fits between the coin and your thumb without being seen by the audience. It must hold enough water to allow you to make the coin 'cry' tears.

SPONGE

2 Once the audience is there, hold up the coin between your thumb and index finger (keeping the wet sponge hidden with your thumb) and tell them a really good story about how some coins are very emotional and you bet you can get this one to cry!

3 Now squeeze the sponge gently, while you yell at the coin. Tears should begin to flow!

4 Once the tears stop, put the sponge and coin in your pocket. If a member of the audience wants to check the coin is real, just pull it out again—minus the sponge, of course.

OH...! WHAT A SAD LITTLE COIN! DID I MAKE YOU CRY?

Trick 16

You need: a handkerchief, a coin, poster putty, a table

In this trick, a coin is placed in the center of a handkerchief in full view of an audience—the magician weaves a magic spell—and it's gone!

1 Before facing your audience, stick a small piece of poster putty to one corner of the handkerchief. This needs to be kept hidden from the audience at all times during the performance.

2 Spread the handkerchief out on the table, keeping hold of the corner that has the putty. Place the coin in the center of the handkerchief and immediately cover it with the corner with the putty.

CORNER WITH POSTER PUTTY

3 Fold the other three corners into the center of the handkerchief over the coin.

4 Place the fingers of both of your hands under the folded edge of the handkerchief which is nearest you. Because of this quick move, the coin, stuck to the handkerchief, ends up in your hand.

5 Show both sides of the handkerchief to the audience, give it a quick shake, and put it in your pocket to finish. Or pretend to blow your nose on it, or pretend to sneeze and cover your nose and mouth with it—anything for a good finale and a round of applause!

6 Perhaps you would like to make this coin reappear? It can be done—of course it can—it's magic! Or it's good planning. Simply have an identical coin hidden somewhere strange—down the top of your sock maybe, or when you remove the coin from the handkerchief, keep it in your hand and then produce it from anywhere you like. Maybe from behind the ear of one of your audience members?

Great... I need a hankie to blow my nose!

Cunning Coin Conundrums

Holey Napkin

Trick 17

You need: a coin, a cloth napkin, a black marker pen

This is a very impressive trick—easy to do and great to watch!

1 Your audience must be seated directly in front of you, as with most tricks! Ask a volunteer for a coin or hand over yours and ask the volunteer to label it with the marker so it will be recognizable later on.

2 Hold the coin upright between the thumb and index finger of your left hand.

3 Place the napkin over the top, so that the coin is in the center of the cloth.

4 Now for the tricky bit—carefully arrange a small fold of the napkin between your thumb and the coin. With your right hand, lift the front of the napkin and drape it back over the top of the napkin and over your left wrist.

COIN
FOLD

5 Make a point of showing your audience the coin is still there.

6 Continue to hold both the coin and the napkin, then flick your left wrist forward which will make both halves of the napkin fall forward.

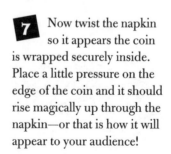

COIN

7 Now twist the napkin so it appears the coin is wrapped securely inside. Place a little pressure on the edge of the coin and it should rise magically up through the napkin—or that is how it will appear to your audience!

You need: four coins of different values, a table

You'll be amazed at how simple this trick is—don't forget to learn some good patter to ensure your audience is really convinced it's magic!

1 Place the four coins on the table while talking about telepathy. Ask an audience member to choose a coin while your back is turned. Tell her to hold it tightly and concentrate hard so you can pick up the vibes from her mind!

4 Turn around and pick up each coin in turn and hold it up to your ear to 'hear' it 'talking' to you. What you're really doing is feeling each coin, because the one which has been held by your volunteer will be much warmer than the others.

2 Concentrate silently for a few moments, pretending you are trying to pick up thought-waves, but what you're really doing is slowly counting to 30.

5 So, once you find the warmest coin, show it to the audience and wait for the applause!

3 When you reach 30, say dispiritedly that you aren't receiving any thoughts from her and accuse her of not concentrating hard enough. Whatever she says, ask for the coin to be put back on the table with the others while you're still not looking, and say that you'll get the coins to tell you which one was selected.

I HEARD THIS ONE SAY... IT'S ME... IT'S ME!

Silky Hanky

You need: a small rubber band, a large, patterned silk square, a ring, a table

This is a simple trick you can do practically anywhere—great for entertaining young children and adults alike! Show them you can make a ring disappear!

1 Before facing your audience, slip a rubber band over three of the fingers on your left hand.

2 Once your audience arrives, take out your silk hanky and wave it about using your right hand so all eyes are on it and not on the rubber band over your fingers! You don't want your audience to notice the rubber band.

3 Spread the hanky over your left hand with a flourish and secretly slip your thumb into the rubber band to widen it a little more.

4 Ask your audience if you can borrow a ring (of course, if they haven't got one you already happen to have one on your table!).

5 Show everyone the ring and then place it on the silk hanky above the rubber band. With your free hand, rub the ring, saying a magic chant. Of course what you are doing is pushing the ring through the band into a fold of silk below.

6 Slip the band off your fingers to trap the ring in a fold in the silk while making a dramatic gesture and saying more magic words.

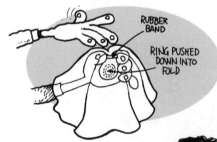

RUBBER BAND

RING PUSHED DOWN INTO FOLD

7 Dramatically whip the hanky away with your right hand and look amazed to see that the ring has disappeared from your left hand.

RING IN FOLD

8 Return the ring by spreading the silk over your left hand again, reach into the folds with your right hand and pull out the ring with a smile!

You need: a long silky scarf, a high-necked top

Most of the classic tricks are very simple, just like this one. The real trick for a magician—
young or old—is to be smooth and professional!

1 Prepare for this trick by tucking the silky scarf into the neck of your high-necked top at the front and sides only.

2 In front of your audience, hold the ends of the scarf securely and pull both ends forward on the count of three, or perhaps while chanting 'Sim sala bim!'

3 To complete the illusion, pull the scarf forward in one quick motion so it appears to pass straight through your neck! Wait for the applause!

SIM SALA BIM!

Did you know?
Harry Houdini died in agony after a student, who had heard he could withstand a powerful blow to the stomach, punched Houdini before he was ready. He was taken to hospital and died a few days later.

Look... you can handcuff me, dangle me over icy rivers in a straitjacket... lock me in a cell and throw away the key. ...BUT PLEASE DON'T HIT ME IN THE TUMMY!

The Magic Cone

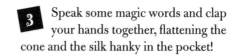

You need: a paper cone with a secret pocket, a silk hanky

It's worth finding a special cone, or making your own for this trick, as it's likely to be one of the best tricks you do. Tell your audience you will make a silk hanky disappear.

1 Unfold the cone so your audience can see it's just a cone (but we know better!) with one decorated side and one plain side.

3 Speak some magic words and clap your hands together, flattening the cone and the silk hanky in the pocket!

2 Fold it back into a cone shape and push the silk hanky into the secret pocket.

4 Unfold the cone carefully and show that there is nothing on the front or back of it—the hanky is gone!

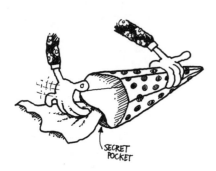

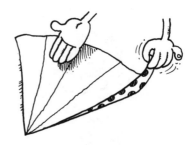

Preparation
Apart from the obvious—learning your tricks so you are really confident performing them—you need to have the props for every trick you will perform. It is a good idea to cover a table with a cloth and put the props on top of the cloth until they are needed. Make sure your props look good!

To do this trick, you'll need to learn a new skill—it's called palming.

1 First, you need to learn to palm the sponge balls—at least they aren't very large! Place one ball in the palm of your hand.  Bring your thumb over a little way to hold it in position; it shouldn't move, even when you hold your hand upright. Practice until you can keep the sponge ball in place when you are moving your hands around a lot. Now try to palm two balls!

2 Once you are really good at palming, you're ready to move on to the next step, which is tricking an audience.

3 Have all three balls in your pocket before you begin your performance. Tell the audience you are getting two balls out of your pocket. Show the audience the two balls in your right hand.

However, you have already palmed a ball, so there are really three balls in your right hand, but the audience must see only two of them.

4 Tell the audience you are moving one ball to your left hand. While you move the ball, secretly move the third ball to your left hand too.

5 Now hold two balls up in the air, one in each hand, and ask your audience to agree that you have one ball in each hand. They will of course. Then pass the ball from your right hand to your left hand, saying as you do: 'Of course, now I have two balls in my left hand, don't I?'

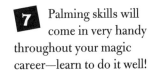

6 But of course, you don't—there are three balls nestling in your hand.

7 Palming skills will come in very handy throughout your magic career—learn to do it well!

OF COURSE IT'S A REAL GRENADE... EVERYTHING IS **REAL** IN MAGIC!

Did you know?
During the Second World War, many magicians entertained the troops. Magicians traveled overseas as well as performing on home ground.

Trick

23

Cups and Balls

This may be the oldest magic trick—hiding a ball under a cup! Magicians all over the world learn it to entertain and confuse their audiences. The special cups used in this trick can be purchased wherever magic props are sold; consider buying a set of clear plastic cups to begin with, so you can see exactly where each ball is as you learn. Each cup has a rim that prevents another cup from being pushed completely inside it, enabling a ball to be hidden in the space created. Also, the bottom of each cup has an indent that allows a soft sponge ball to rest without rolling off.

1 To prepare, place the large ball in your left pocket and one small ball in each of the three cups, and the fourth small ball

in your left hand. The cups are then placed inside each other. They should be sitting mouth-up.

2 When you begin the performance, turn each cup over quickly, keeping the ball hidden underneath.

3 Tap or wave your hand over all the cups and then lift the right one with your right hand to reveal a ball resting on the table underneath it. Transfer the cup to your left hand, so it covers the small ball hidden there.

4 Repeat with the other two cups, showing the two other balls, and placing the cups over the one already in your left hand.

5 Now place each cup mouth-down directly behind a ball on the table. Place the last cup you lifted behind the right ball. Place the second cup you lifted behind the left ball. Place the first cup you lifted behind the center ball. As you place this cup on the table, make sure the concealed ball drops into it before you turn it mouth-down.

6 Pick up the center ball and place it on top of the center cup. Next, place both the other cups on top of the ball. With a tap or wave of your hand, lift all three cups as one to reveal a ball on the table. To the audience it appears as though you have magically made the ball pass through the base of the cup. Wait for the applause, and then say: 'But wait, there's more!'

7 Hold the stack of cups mouth-up so the hidden ball is now resting inside the middle cup. Separate the cups again and place the empty ones mouth-down on the table, behind the right and left balls. Put the cup with the ball mouth-down over the center ball. Place a ball on top of this cup and repeat step 6, inviting a volunteer to tap the cup. While your volunteer is doing this, take the large ball from your pocket and hold it in your left hand.

8 When you lift the stack of cups again, astonishingly, three small balls are on the table. Casually place the cups mouth-down in your left hand and act as though the trick is finished by placing the stack of cups mouth-down on the table.

9 A bit of acting here will earn you enormous applause, so hesitate as if you want to tell your audience something, but shouldn't. Then say you'll reveal a magic secret: you did use more than three balls for the trick! Pick up the cups to reveal a much larger ball—to more applause!

You need: a photocopy of a large clock, a pencil

Find a really great clock face to photocopy, because the more zany it is, the more it will distract your audience from the simple, but clever, trick you are about to do for them.

1 Ask a volunteer to look at the photocopied clock face and select a number from it—silently! Ask your volunteer to add 1 to the number she selects, so if she chooses 7, she adds 1 to make 8, keeping this all in her head.

2 If she needs to write down the number she first thought of, let her do so, but make sure you can't see it.

3 Now for the clever bit! Ask your volunteer to begin counting silently from the number she now has (so the next number is 9) each time you tap your pencil on the clock's face.

4 When she gets to 20, she is to say 'Stop!' Remarkably, you will be on the correct number, so you circle it on the clock's face and hand it to your volunteer face-down. She is to tell the audience the number she originally selected and then turn over the page to reveal your answer. Your answer will be correct every time!

5 The secret? Well, it is that you begin tapping on the clock's face at the number 6 each time you do the trick and you tap counter-clockwise on the numbers. When your volunteer says 'stop' after reaching 20, you will always be on the correct number—it's magic!

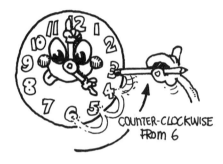

COUNTER-CLOCKWISE FROM 6

6 If you are going to repeat this trick in front of the same audience, make sure no one sees where you begin tapping each time.

Famous Names

Trick 25

You need: ten cards big enough to write names on but small enough to fit into the magic hat, a pencil, a piece of paper, a hat

You'll choose the correct name every time, but you can only do this trick once per audience!

1 Ask people in your audience to call out ten famous names. As they do, write each name on a card and place it in the hat. Well, that's what your audience thinks you're doing! What you are really doing is repeatedly writing down the first name called, perhaps it was Nelson Mandela. Write that on a card, place it in the hat, and pretend to write down the next nine names called out—maybe you'll hear Madonna, Tom Cruise, and Shakespeare and others shouted out—but every time you write down Nelson Mandela and put the card in the hat!

2 Now of course it's easy. You ask someone from the audience to come up and pick a name out of the hat, read it but not tell anyone.

3 You ask your volunteer to concentrate hard on the name and you do the same, making sure you act as if it is very hard to do! After a few seconds of this, tell the audience you now believe you can read the volunteer's mind and the answer is 'Nelson Mandela'.

4 Everyone will be astounded and will cheer and clap wildly. On no account are you to repeat this trick with the same audience—for obvious reasons!

When performing this great trick, a smart magician must remember that the opposite sides of a dice always add up to seven.

1 Use a lot of theatrics when performing this trick, because the trick really does itself. Show the audience the three dice, the pen and the paper, and ask for a volunteer to help you.

2 While you stand at the back of the stage with your back to the audience, ask the volunteer to roll the three dice, pick them up in any order, and stack them one on top of the other.

3 Continue keeping your back to the audience and ask the volunteer to carefully add up the numbers of the five hidden faces of the dice (see illustration). The volunteer now writes down this number and silently shows it to the audience.

4 Once the audience has seen the paper with the number on it, the volunteer should tear it up. Now you should turn around and face the audience. Move to the table and stare at the stacked dice.

5 Bring your hands to your head—pretend that you are concentrating— and announce the correct answer to wild applause!

6 The secret to this trick is that the opposite sides of a dice always add up to seven. You have three dice, so 7 multiplied by 3 equals 21. When you turn and step forward, you look at the number on the top dice, let's say it is 5. Take 5 away from 21 and you get 16. Tell your audience that 16 is the number on the piece of paper—and you'll be absolutely correct.

$$7 \times 3 = 21$$
$$5 \text{ ON TOP}$$
$$21 - 5 = 16$$

$$
\begin{array}{r}
2 \\
+ \\
4 \\
+ \\
3 \\
+ \\
1 \\
+ \\
6 \\
\hline
= 16
\end{array}
$$

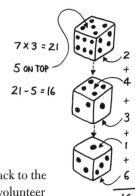

7 Standing with your back to the audience, having the volunteer tear up the paper and acting as if you were struggling with the answer are all showmanship— the answer is always right in front of you!

Trick 27

Book Test

You need: a paperback book about 180–200 pages long, a playing card or a business card

This trick relies on you making it look as if you are doing one thing when you are actually doing another!

1 Either hand your own book to an audience member, or ask for a paperback book to be loaned to you for the trick—a borrowed book will make your magical skills seem even greater!

2 Ask the audience member to flick through the pages to check that each page is different and that the book is genuine and has not been tampered with in any way.

3 Give him the playing card or business card and ask him to turn to any page in the book. Now ask him to look at the page number and the last word on that page and to concentrate hard on them. You should watch and see if he is looking at a right-hand or left-hand page. Now ask your volunteer to insert the playing card or business card into the book and hand it back to you.

4 Now this is the part where you must be seen to be doing one thing, while actually doing another. What you are going to do is chat with the audience about what has happened so far, and while you do this you flick through each and every page of the book, talking about how many thousands of words it must contain. You mention how you need your volunteer to continue to think of the last word on the page he selected, otherwise you'll have little hope of choosing the right word despite your great mental skills.

5 Of course, what you are really doing as you flick through the pages is using the inserted card to your advantage. As you flick your thumb will briefly stop at the page where the card is inserted. Your thumb will jump to the opposite page and in that brief moment you glance down, noting the page number and the last word on either the right-hand or left-hand page (depending on which one your volunteer was looking at). You must then continue to flick through the pages, talking all the time about your mental skills and your ability to divine other people's thoughts.

GLANCE DOWN AS QUICK AS A FLASH!

6 Once you know the page number and the last word you should ask your volunteer to try harder to 'send' the correct word to you telepathically. After a suitable length of time, you correctly tell the audience the page number and the last word.

7 This trick really relies on your patter and your ability to keep your audience believing you aren't looking through the book! Make sure you practice this one—it seems easy and it is, but the skill is in making it look very natural.

Rope Handcuffs

Trick
28

You'll tie your audience up in knots with this trick! (Then you'll free them, of course!)

1 Ask for two brave volunteers. Tie their wrists together with the ropes as shown in the illustration.

2 Now ask them to try really hard to release themselves from their predicament without cutting the ropes or untying the knots. Of course they won't be able to do so and now you'll have to help them.

3 First, pull the middle of one of the ropes towards the opposite person so you create a loop. Now draw the loop to the wrist of that person and pass the loop through the rope around the wrist and pull it over the entire hand.

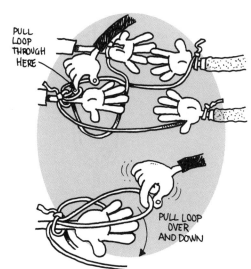

PULL LOOP THROUGH HERE

PULL LOOP OVER AND DOWN

4 Once this has occurred you have actually freed your volunteers from their rope handcuffs—ask them to step back from each other and take the wild applause gracefully!

Fun Facts
The most famous rope trick is the Indian Rope Trick. In this trick, a magician throws a long rope into the air, but the rope does not fall. Instead it stands erect, vertically in the air. The magician's assistant, normally a young boy, then climbs the rope to the top and disappears. Though the trick is considered a hoax now, many magicians have tried to duplicate the trick for many years!

Just One Hand

You need: one length of rope measuring 90 cm (35 in.)

This is another simple trick that audiences love to watch—you'll tie a knot in a rope using just one hand—and they won't know how you did it!

1 Make sure your audience sits directly in front of you. Now drape the rope across your right hand, between the thumb and index finger and behind the little finger. One end needs to be a little longer than the other (see illustration depicting A and B).

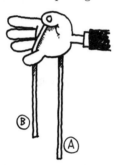

2 Give the rope an upward flick and drop your hand down at the same time. You should catch the longer end of the rope (A) between your index and middle fingers.

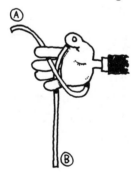

3 Now hold onto the A end of the rope and turn your hand so your fingers are facing the floor. The rest of the rope will slip off your hand, forming a one-handed knot!

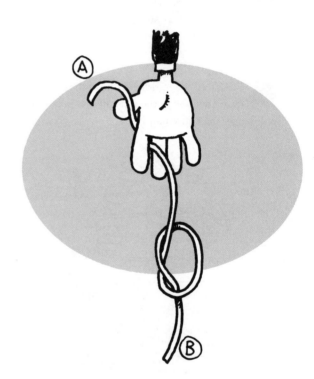

4 You will have to practice that upward flick—but it's worth it, as it's a classy trick when done correctly!

Oooh...Aye ABRACADABRA! I think we might try a wee rabbit here. This haggis is not really doin' the trick!

Did you know?
Pulling a rabbit out of a hat is supposed to be a classic trick. However, it's a trick that is rarely performed. It was probably devised by Scottish magician John Henry Anderson in the 1830s.

You need: a piece of rope at least 90 cm (35 in.) long, a table, a wand, a jacket with an inside pocket

Your friends won't mind being strung along with this clever rope trick.

1 Show your audience you are holding a short piece of rope. (In fact, you are holding the ends of your long piece of rope, but more on that later.) Explain that your powers can make the rope grow.

3 You can continue to pull the rope, or even better, ask a volunteer to do so for you. Once it is coiled on the table, take a bow as your audience applauds.

2 Tap the back of your hand with your wand and say some terrific magic words and then begin to pull the rope from one end. It will continue to grow and grow and grow.

4 How is it done? It's simple really. Fold the rope in half and make sure both ends are held in your hand. Thread the rest of the rope up your jacket sleeve and into the inside pocket.

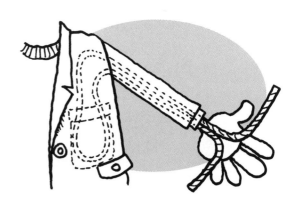

Cut and Restored Rope

You need: a piece of soft rope about 1.2 m (4 ft) long, scissors

This is a classic trick all magicians need to perfect. You will appear to cut a piece of rope in half, then restore it.

1 Once more, make sure your audience is seated directly in front of you. Drape the center of the rope over your index finger.

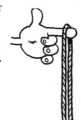

2 Bring one end of the rope up to the middle and tie a square knot.

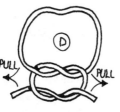

3 Explain that you have magic scissors, then with a flourish cut the rope. You must cut it in exactly the place shown in the illustration.

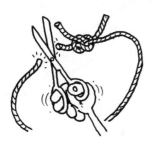

4 Once the cut has been made, casually put the scissors down in a place where the audience cannot see them. Now hold the cotton rope at each end and pull it tightly so everyone can see it's a rope with a knot in the center.

5 Begin to wrap the rope around one of your hands—your left if you are right-handed, your right if you are left-handed. As you wrap the rope, the square knot will slide off the rope and must be concealed in your hand. Reach for your magic scissors, while you quickly drop the piece of rope out of sight.

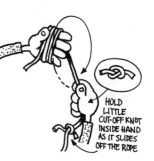

HOLD LITTLE CUT-OFF KNOT INSIDE HAND AS IT SLIDES OFF THE ROPE

6 Wave your magic scissors over your wrapped hand and recite your favorite magic words. Put down the scissors—this time in full view of your audience—unwrap the rope and wave it about. The rope is restored!

ABRACADABRA

You need: a pocketful of change

Although you need many coins for this trick—you use none! Your audience will think you are throwing a coin from hand to hand, but it's all an illusion!

1 Make a show of taking a handful of coins from your pocket—let the audience see the coins are real. Choose one coin and pretend to pick it up—you'll need to practice this! Return the coins to your pocket.

2 Throw the imaginary coin back and forth from one hand to the other, making a small slapping sound as you pretend to catch the coin each time. Practice with a real coin so you can get the sound right, but if you loosen your fingers and slap the heel of your palm as you 'catch' your coin, it should sound OK.

3 Do this several times, then stop and pretend to hold the imaginary coin in one hand. Ask your audience to guess how it landed—'Heads or tails?' Of course, upon opening your hand there is no coin. That's OK because the audience assumes it's now in your other hand.

4 Slowly open your other hand to reveal no coin there either—and bow while your audience applauds!

ONLY PRETEND THERE'S A COIN

SLAP FINGERS HERE FOR A SLAP SOUND

SLAP

LIKE A COIN HITTING YOUR PALM!

BANG

You should know enough about MAGIC now to know just how I do this trick..! 1... 2....3...

You need: a deck of cards, a large scarf (or handkerchief)

You're such a good magician that any card you name can penetrate a solid object, such as a scarf!

1 All you have to do beforehand is secretly memorize the top card in the deck and then remember not to shuffle the cards!

MEMORIZED CARD NOW ON BOTTOM OF DECK

2 Hold the deck face-up in the palm of your left hand if you're right-handed, or in your right if you are left-handed. The card you have memorized should be sitting on the bottom of the deck in your palm.

3 Show the scarf to the audience—in fact, pass it around so everyone can see it's an ordinary scarf.

4 Once it's returned to you, drape the scarf over the deck of cards so its center rests on top of the deck.

5 Make sure you draw the audience's attention to the fact you can't see the cards because the scarf is covering the deck. Now, reach under the scarf with your other hand and remove the deck, but leave the memorized card behind in your palm.

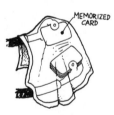

MEMORIZED CARD

6 Place the deck of cards on top of the scarf, directly over the card that is hidden under the scarf.

7 Begin to wrap the deck of cards in the scarf. Start by folding the edge nearest you away from you with your free hand. Place the thumb of this hand underneath the card in your opposite palm and the wrapped deck. Place the rest of the fingers in your opposite palm on top to grip the deck, and now revolve it upright so the hidden card faces you. Do this part carefully, because if you allow the hidden card to shift the audience will see it!

8 Now, keeping the hand gripping the package where it is, use your opposite hand to fold the sides of the scarf back towards you, diagonally over the hidden card. The folds need to overlap this card, while your thumb holds everything in place.

9 It's time to dazzle your audience! With the fist of the hand that folded the scarf, grip all of the scarf hanging below and rotate the deck (keeping the hidden card facing you) so it is hanging down. If the folds are tight enough, the hidden card should stay in place when you lift your thumb.

10 Tell your audience that you can magically make any card you call appear through the scarf. Now, of course, you call to the card you have memorized—the hidden card—and then shake the deck, while chanting magic words. The hidden card will magically begin to appear as if it is penetrating the center of the scarf. When it hits the table, allow the wrapped deck to be examined as you are basking in your audience's admiration!

SHAKE SHAKE

COOL FREAKY FACTS

COOL FREAKY FACTS

When Louis Armstrong sang 'What a Wonderful World', he might have been singing about all the amazing and astonishing facts that surround us every day. From unusual animals to weird phobias and even the language that you use every day, freaky facts are all around, just waiting for you to discover.

In this section, we've included lots of facts to share, all true, that will shock and startle you as you learn more and more about the wonderful world around you!

Contents

1 The only bird that can fly backwards is the hummingbird.

2 The giant squid has the largest eyes in the world.

3 A goldfish has a memory span of three seconds.

4 Toupees for dogs are sold in Tokyo.

5 A dolphin sleeps with one eye open.

6 A crocodile cannot stick its tongue out.

7 A mammal's blood is red, an insect's blood is yellow, and a lobster's blood is blue.

8 Loud, fast music makes termites chew faster.

9 Bats always exit a cave to the left.

10 Tigers have striped skin, not just striped fur.

Unusual Animal Facts

11 Herons have been observed dropping insects on the water, then catching the fish that surface to eat the insects.

The not so smart Heron comes to the realization that if dropping insects on the water attracts teensy weensy fish...it may also attract older hungrier not so friendly relatives as well.

12 The largest egg is laid by the ostrich. An ostrich egg can be 8 in. (20 cm) in length and 6 in. (15 cm) in diameter.

13 The smallest egg is laid by the hummingbird. Its egg is less than 0.39 in. (1 cm) in diameter.

14 A blind chameleon is still able to change the color of its skin to match its environment.

OK..OK! Who's the wiseguy? I don't do that background!

15 A zebra is white with black stripes, not black with white stripes.

16 Statistically you are more likely to be attacked by a cow than a shark.

AHHRR! QUICK! Everyone out! There's a COW in the water!

17 At birth, a giant panda is smaller than a mouse.

18 To scare off enemies, the horned lizard squirts blood from its eyelids.

19 Spider silk, by weight, is stronger than steel.

20 Horses can sleep standing up.

21 An electric eel can produce a shock of 600 volts. That's enough to knock a horse off its feet.

22 Lobsters can regenerate their legs, claws and antennae if these parts are pulled off by a predator.

23 Parrots live longer than any other type of bird. There are reliable reports of parrots living to 150 years of age.

24 An African elephant has only four teeth.

25 Sea snakes are the most venomous snakes.

26 A scallop swims by quickly clapping its shell open and shut. This makes a water jet that pushes the scallop along.

27 Some captive octopus have learned to open jars containing food. Many aquariums now give their octopuses puzzles and other games to keep them from getting bored.

Oscar, an octopus with plenty of time on his hands, contemplates an escape from the tank.

28 Polar bears have been known to swim 62 miles (100 km) without stopping.

29 An ant can lift ten times its own weight.

30 Salamanders breathe through their skin.

Freaky Facts

31 There are more plastic flamingos in the USA than real ones.

32 A giraffe has the same number of vertebrae in its neck as a mouse.

33 Turkeys often look up at the sky during a rainstorm. Unfortunately, some have drowned as a result.

34 The Loch Ness Monster is a protected animal under Scottish law.

35 A snail can sleep for three years.

36 Sheep can recognize other sheep from photographs.

37 Bees have five eyes.

38 Honeybees kill more people than venomous snakes do.

39 Polar bears are left-handed.

40 A zebra foal can run with the herd an hour after its birth.

41 A polar bear's fur is not white, but translucent.

42 Butterflies taste with their feet.

43 The polar bear is the only mammal with hair on the soles of its feet.

44 American President John Quincy Adams owned a pet alligator. He kept it in the East Room of the White House.

45 Female ants do all the work.

46 A cockroach can live up to two weeks with its head cut off before it starves to death.

47 Walruses turn pink if they stay out in the sun too long.

48 A beaver can hold its breath underwater for up to 45 minutes.

49 Vultures have a unique defence mechanism; they throw up on their enemies.

50 A female pigeon cannot lay an egg unless she sees another pigeon. If another pigeon is not available, her own reflection in a mirror will do.

Freaky Facts

51 Female canaries cannot sing.

52 Cockroaches could survive a nuclear holocaust because radiation does not affect them as much as it affects other species.

53 The embryos of tiger sharks fight each other while in their mother's womb. Only the survivor is born.

54 Australian earthworms can grow up to 10 ft (3 m) in length.

55 Elephants and humans are the only animals that can stand on their heads.

56 There is enough poison in a poison-arrow frog to kill 2200 people.

57 A camel can drink up to 30 gallons (136 litres) of water at one time.

58 Racehorses can wear out new horseshoes in just one race.

59 If a starfish is cut into pieces, each piece will become another starfish.

60 A dolphin can hear sound underwater from 15 miles (24 km) away.

61 Watermelons are grown square in Japan so they take up less space and are easier to stack.

62 An apple, potato, and onion all taste sweet if you eat them with your nose plugged.

63 Jupiter is bigger than all the other planets in our solar system combined.

64 Natural gas has no smell. The smell is added for safety reasons.

65 Strawberries contain more vitamin C than oranges.

66 Forty-one per cent of the moon is not visible from Earth at any time.

67 The age of the universe is 13.7 billion years.

THE UNIVERSE TURNS 13.7 BILLION

68 Ninety per cent of all extinct species are birds.

69 Sound travels through water three times faster than through air.

WHY 90% OF ALL EXTINCT SPECIES ...ARE BIRDS!

70 The largest flower in the world is the corpse flower or *Rafflesia*. It grows up to 4 ft (1.2 m) wide and it stinks.

71 There are eight peas per pod on average.

72 Raindrops are not really shaped like drops; they are perfectly round.

In his quest to find out whether rain drops are perfectly round, Timothy stood in the rain for 24 hours ...not catching any raindrops...but catching a cold instead.

AAAAAHR

73 Lemons contain more sugar than strawberries.

Why are you sucking on lemons?

I don't know! I must be crazy! For something that contains more sugar than strawberries ...they don't taste too sweet!

74 The Amazon rainforest makes one-fifth of the world's oxygen.

75 The Antarctic ice sheet contains 71 per cent of the world's fresh water.

76 Water is the only substance on Earth that is lighter as a solid than as a liquid.

77 Coconuts kill more people than sharks do. Approximately 150 people are killed each year by coconuts.

AHHRR! EVERYBODY OUT! THERE'S COCONUTS IN THE WATER!!

Remember the days when people would run screaming from the water because of us?

Yeah. Then someone worked out that coconuts killed more people than sharks!

78 Antarctica is the only place on Earth that is not owned by any country.

79 The only food that does not spoil is honey.

80 Australia is the only continent on Earth without an active volcano.

81 Fingernails grow nearly four times faster than toenails.

82 By raising your legs slowly and lying on your back, you cannot sink in quicksand.

83 The opposite sides of a dice always add up to seven.

84 Woodpecker scalps, porpoise teeth, and giraffe tails have all been used as money.

85 A jiffy is an actual unit of time. It is 1/100 of a second.

86 There are more than 600 million telephone lines in the world.

87 Twenty per cent of all road accidents in Sweden involve a moose.

Twenty percent of all road accidents in Sweden involve a MOOSE.

88 More than 1000 languages are spoken in Africa.

89 A porcupine has about 30 000 quills.

90 Humans have 639 muscles, but caterpillars have more than 4000.

91 If you could drive to the sun at 55 miles (90 km) per hour, it would take about 193 years.

92 Every five seconds, a baby is born.

93 Just twenty seconds' worth of fuel remained when Apollo 11's lunar module landed on the moon.

Crunching Numbers

94 A solar day on Mercury, from sunrise to sunset, lasts about six Earth months.

95 There are more than 14 000 varieties of rice.

96 Cats can spend 16 hours a day sleeping.

After what amounted to sleeping most of the day, Harry the Persian slept most of the night catching up on the sleep he missed during the day.

97 It takes 72 muscles to speak one word.

98 An alligator has 80 teeth.

As Albert climbed from the swamb...he recalled the newsclipping he'd read on alligators having 80 teeth...and every one of them being very sharp.

99 It takes approximately 850 peanuts to make a standard jar of peanut butter.

100 The Great Wall of China is 2149 miles (3460 km) long.

101 Summer and winter on Uranus each last 21 Earth years.

102 McDonald's makes 40 per cent of its profits from Happy Meals.

103 The Earth travels around the sun at about 67 000 miles (107 000 km) per hour.

104 One in five children in the world has never been inside a schoolroom.

105 On average, 18 acres of pizza are eaten every day in the USA.

106 A dragonfly lives for one day.

107 There are more insects in a 1 mile (1.6 km) square of rural land than there are people on the planet.

DON'T MOVE SHIRLEY OLD GIRL! Do you realize that if you do.... you might squash more bugs than there are people in China!

108 The human heart creates enough pressure to squirt blood over 30 ft (9 m).

109 A dairy cow will give about 200 000 glasses of milk in its lifetime.

110 The main library at Indiana University sinks over 1 in. (2.5 cm) every year. When it was built, engineers failed to take into account the weight of the books that would occupy the building.

111 There are 18 doctors in the USA called Dr. Doctor, and one called Dr. Surgeon.

112 Twenty thousand men took 22 years to build the Taj Mahal.

113 Bolivia has two capital cities.

114 The height of the Eiffel Tower varies by as much as 6 in. (15 cm), depending on the temperature.

115 Mickey Mouse received 800 000 pieces of fan mail in 1933.

The library at Indiana University finally sinks under the weight of the books after C.J. returns his three overdue library books.

INDIANA UNIVERSITY LIBRARY

It was only two pretty light paperbacks and a comic book!

Crunching Numbers

116 The blue whale, the largest animal ever, is 100 ft (30 m) long. It weighs as much as 4 large dinosaurs, 23 elephants, 230 cows or 1800 men.

117 The name Hitler was listed 22 times in the New York phone book before World War II. After the war, the name was not listed once.

118 Almost one-quarter of all mammal species on Earth are bats.

119 Lightning is five times hotter than the surface of the sun.

120 The Earth is 4.5 billion years old.

121 Wearing headphones can increase the bacteria in your ears by up to 700 times.

122 It takes about 63 000 trees to make the Sunday edition of the *New York Times*.

123 Pain travels through the human body at a speed of over 350 ft (106 m) per second.

124 The sun makes up 99 per cent of the matter in our solar system.

125 The average person spends three years of their life on the toilet.

126 The average number of people in aircraft over the USA in any given hour is 61 000.

127 A person drinks about 20 000 gallons (75 000 litres) of water in his lifetime.

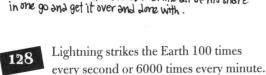

After hearing that a person drinks 20,000 gallons of water in a lifetime... Arnold decided to drink all of his share in one go and get it over and done with.

128 Lightning strikes the Earth 100 times every second or 6000 times every minute.

129 You share your birthday with more than nine million people.

130 The wingspan of a Boeing 747 is longer than the Wright brothers' first flight.

Keep the nose up Wilbur! We've got to make it across this... What is that? A big plane?

Hang on Orville, Turn off the engine. Why are we bothering to even try for the first powered flight? Somebody's already beaten us to it!

131 No piece of dry, square paper can be folded in half more than seven times.

132 Recycling one glass jar saves enough energy to power a television for three hours.

After learning on TV that recycling one glass jar could power a television for one hour... Debbie figured that gobbling down a jar of pickled onions.. a jar of anchovies and a half jar of pickled gherkins would give her at least a full day of TV.

133 In one day your heart beats 100 000 times.

134 The Empire State Building consists of more than ten million bricks.

135 The longest conga line had 119 986 people in it.

136 The average bank teller loses about $250 every year.

137 Scientists estimate that there are at least 15 million stars for every person on Earth.

Freaky Facts

138 There are ten towns named Hollywood in the USA.

139 It is estimated that 6800 languages are spoken in the world today.

140 In the average lifetime a person will breathe in nearly 44 lb (20 kg) of dust.

Shake off as many old dusty rugs as you like around me... Vacuum your dirty old carpets... Dust down that dusty furniture... and don't forget the TV... Just don't ask me to run anywhere with this mask on though

141 You blink over ten million times in a year.

142 Rats multiply so quickly that in 18 months, two rats could have more than one million descendants.

I'm sorry to say dear... And I don't know how to tell you this... But I think we've got a RAT PROBLEM! Our family has..... well... bred like rats!

I know! There must be a million of them! I lost track of their names after the first couple of hundred thousand!

143 A butterfly has more than 12 000 lenses in each eye.

144 The combined wealth of the world's 250 richest people is greater than the combined wealth of the poorest 1.5 billion people.

145 Outer space begins 50 miles (80 km) above the Earth.

146 When awake, cats spend up to 30 per cent of their time grooming.

Rex... always an excessive cat as a kitten, was not content with the average 30% of his time spent grooming... He went for the full 100%

147 An elephant can smell water nearly 3 miles (5 km) away.

148 A hippopotamus can open its mouth 4 ft (1.2 m) wide.

149 The sperm whale's intestines are over 450 ft (137 m) long.

150 'Twinkle Twinkle Little Star' was written by Mozart.

151 The first time a toilet was shown on television was in the show 'Leave It to Beaver'.

152 Leonardo da Vinci spent 12 years painting the *Mona Lisa*'s lips.

153 Walt Disney was afraid of mice.

154 Barbie's full name is Barbara Millicent Roberts.

155 Sherlock Holmes never said 'Elementary, my dear Watson'.

156 Marcel the monkey was fired from the television show 'Friends' because of his nasty habit of vomiting live worms.

157 Soccer is the most popular sport in the world.

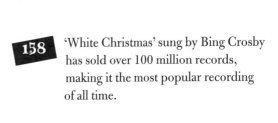

158 'White Christmas' sung by Bing Crosby has sold over 100 million records, making it the most popular recording of all time.

159 Donald Duck comics were once banned in Finland because Donald does not wear pants.

160 *Tom Sawyer* was the first novel written on a typewriter.

Freaky Facts

161 The Bible has been translated into Klingon.

162 Boxing is the most popular theme in movies about sport.

Give him a right upper cut.'

Go on! Nail him!'

Get in with a right hook... go on... a right hook!'

Max makes a big mistake in believing the movie 'The Ring' was going to be a fantasy.

163 The first four countries to have television were England, the USA, the USSR, and Brazil.

That's supposed to be our Prime Minister welcoming us to television! Does that look like the Prime Minister to you George? It certainly doesn't to me!'

THE DAY **BEFORE** TELEVISION STARTED IN BRITAIN.

164 The song 'Rudolph the Red-Nosed Reindeer' was invented in 1939 for a department store promotion.

165 'The Muppet Show' was banned in Saudi Arabia because one of its stars was a pig.

166 Alfred Hitchcock did not have a belly button. It was eliminated when he was sewn up after surgery.

167 Dolly Parton once lost a Dolly Parton lookalike contest.

168 In 1938, the creators of Superman sold the rights to the character for $65 each.

169 Vincent Van Gogh only sold one painting in his life and that was to his brother.

170 More Monopoly money than real money is printed in a year.

171 The first time a toilet was flushed in a movie was in *Psycho*.

LIGHTS... CAMERA... ACTION! PUSH THAT BUTTON!'

The not so famous toilet flushing scene from the movie Psycho... Filmed just before the more well known... shower scene.

172 Cleopatra was Greek, not Egyptian.

173 In 1867, the Russian Czar Alexander II sold Alaska for about $7.2 million to the USA to pay off his gambling debts. At the time, most people thought this was a really bad deal for the USA.

174 In the Middle Ages, pepper was used for bartering, and it was often more valuable than gold.

175 The oldest restaurant still in business opened in China in 1153.

176 Napoleon constructed his battle plans in a sandbox.

Napoleon plans the Battle of Waterloo in a sandbox.

177 Athletes in the ancient Olympics competed in the nude.

178 The Japanese throne has been occupied by a member of the same family since the sixth century. The present emperor is the 125th in succession.

179 The umbrella originated in ancient Egypt, where it was used by the royal family and nobles as a symbol of rank.

180 The Vikings reached North America 500 years before the Pilgrims.

181 The Tower of London is currently the home of the British crown jewels. It has been a zoo, an observatory, a mint, and a prison.

182 Napoleon Bonaparte designed the Italian flag.

183 Before 1800, separate shoes for right and left feet were not designed.

Edward tries out the first pair of left and right shoes in 1800.

184 The cigarette lighter was invented before the match.

185 Tea is believed to have been discovered in 2737 BC by a Chinese emperor when some tea leaves accidentally blew into a pot of boiling water.

186 Henry III became king when he was ten months old.

187 King George I of England could not speak English.

188 Mexico once had three different presidents in 24 hours.

189 A squirrel closed down the New York stock exchange one day in 1987 when it burrowed through a phone line.

190 Sunglasses were invented by the Chinese in the thirteenth century.

191 Denmark has the oldest existing national flag. The flag dates back to the thirteenth century.

192 Big Ben, a clock in London, once lost time when a group of birds used the minute hand as a perch.

193 Before 1600, New Year's Day was in March.

194 In the tenth century, the Grand Vizier of Persia carried his library on 400 trained camels. The camels had to walk in alphabetical order.

200 The Sumerians, who lived in the Middle East, invented the wheel in about 3450 BC.

195 In ancient Japan, public contests were held to see who could fart the loudest and longest.

201 The wheelbarrow was invented in ancient China.

196 The story of Cinderella originated in China.

197 The most popular game ever for coin-operated machines is Pac-Man.

198 Coca-Cola was originally green.

202 Illegal gambling houses in eighteenth-century England employed a person to swallow the dice if there was a police raid.

199 The oldest existing governing body, the Althing, operates in Iceland. It was established in AD 930.

203 The first message sent over Graham Bell's telephone on 10 March 1876 was 'Mr Watson, come here, I want you'.

204 In the Philippines during the 1500s, the yo-yo was made of stone and used as a weapon.

205 Ancient Egyptians slept on pillows made of stone.

206 Bread was used as an eraser before rubber erasers were invented.

207 Since its discovery in 1930, Pluto has completed only about 20 per cent of its orbit. The last time Pluto was in its present position was before the American Revolution.

208 Napoleon Bonaparte was afraid of cats.

209 In *Gulliver's Travels*, Jonathan Swift described the two moons of Mars, giving their exact sizes and speeds of rotation. He did this more than 100 years before the moons were discovered.

210 Long ago, clans that wanted to get rid of unpopular people would burn their houses down, hence the expression 'to get fired'.

211 The word 'checkmate' in chess comes from the Persian phrase 'Shah Mat', which means 'the king is dead'.

212 Early Greeks and Romans used dried watermelons for helmets.

213 Karate originated in India, but was developed further in China.

214 The Earth spins at 1000 miles (1600 km) per hour at the equator.

215 The Earth rotates more slowly on its axis in March than in September.

216 Europe is the only continent without a desert.

217 Diamonds are flammable.

218 In Japan, there are vending machines for underwear.

219 Candles burn better when they are frozen.

220 The largest continent is Asia.

221 The South Pole is colder than the North Pole.

222 The USA creates nearly 20 per cent of the world's garbage.

223 The first living creature to orbit the Earth was a dog sent into space by the Russians.

224 A storm officially becomes a hurricane when it reaches wind speeds of 74 miles (119 km) per hour.

You know when strong wind becomes a hurricane when the windspeed reaches 74 miles per hour.... or... when cows and cars start flying past you.

225 The Greek national anthem has 158 verses.

226 The moon moves 1.5 in. (3.82 cm) away from the Earth every year.

227 Damascus in Syria is the oldest inhabited city. It was founded in 753 BC.

228 Australia is the only country that takes up an entire continent.

229 In Bangladesh, school children can be jailed for cheating on their exams.

230 Half the world's population is under 25 years old.

231 The deepest part of the Pacific Ocean is 6.8 miles (11 km).

232 The most abundant metal in the ground is aluminum.

233 Every year in Sweden, a hotel is built out of ice. It melts, then it is rebuilt the next year.

234 In Vietnam, there is a drink made from lizard blood.

235 Chewing gum can keep a person from crying while cutting onions.

I was about to start cutting these onions... and now I've trod in this awful chewing gum.

Little Rupert couldn't bear to see his Mum cry while cutting onions. So spitting his gum on the floor did the trick. She couldn't cut the onions.

236 Black pepper is the most popular spice in the world.

237 Banana plants cannot reproduce themselves. They must be propagated by people.

238 Unless you have a doctor's note, it is illegal to buy ice cream after 6 p.m. in Newark, New Jersey.

239 Nachos is the food most often craved by pregnant women.

240 Canned food was invented in 1813, but a practical can opener was not invented until 1870.

If you'd like baked beans for your breakfast, take this can outside and hit it with this rock until it opens.

BEANS

241 Because Hindus do not eat beef, McDonald's in New Delhi makes lamb hamburgers.

242 The blue whale needs to consume 1.5 million calories a day.

243 Peanuts are one of the ingredients in dynamite.

244 Koalas do not drink water.

We koalas don't drink water. But some of us don't mind the occasional lemonade... or cola.... As long as it's not water.' Anything cold really.... Oh... And through a straw please!

245 A favorite meal in China is sun-dried maggots.

246 Most cows give more milk when they listen to music.

247 Rain contains vitamin B12.

248 You are more likely to be killed by a champagne cork than by a venomous spider.

249 Astronauts are not allowed to eat beans before they go into space because passing wind in a spacesuit damages it.

So that definitely was a can of beans I saw you smuggling on board the rocket before blast-off!

250 Most lipsticks contain fish scales.

251 Eating an apple will make you feel more awake in the morning than drinking a cup of coffee will.

And now if we can raise our glasses for a toast to the bride and groom... AHHRR... A SPIDER!

Despite a venomous spider being on the loose at the wedding... It was the bride's father with a champagne bottle they really had to fear.

252 No words in the English language rhyme with month, orange, silver, or purple.

253 'Go' is the shortest sentence in the English language.

254 The Cambodian alphabet is the largest. It has 74 letters.

255 The Hawaiian alphabet consists of only 12 letters.

256 The longest word in English is 'pneumonoultramicroscopicsilicovol-canoconiosis'.

257 The Inuit (Eskimos) have 20 different words for snow.

258 Dr Seuss invented the word 'nerd'.

259 'Zorro' is Spanish for 'fox'.

The great Mexican super hero...Zorro (the fox)

260 The first word spoken on the moon was 'Okay'.

261 The oldest word in the English language is 'town'.

262 More people in China speak English than in the USA.

263 The dot over the letter 'i' is called the tittle.

The dot at the end of the sentence is a full stop. The dot above the letter i is called a tittle. And the rest of the stuff all over your page is called ... a MESS!

264 'Of' is the only word in which an 'f' is pronounced like a 'v'.

265 A pregnant goldfish is called a twit.

266 The word 'taxi' is spelled the same in English, German, French, Swedish, and Portuguese.

267 The sentence 'the quick brown fox jumps over the lazy dog' uses every letter in the alphabet.

268 The word 'Mrs' cannot be written in full.

Woh! I thought that lazy hound was asleep!

WOOF!

'The quick brown fox jumps over the lazy dog' uses every letter in the alphabet. ... But add...'The lazy dog wasn't asleep ...he was only pretending' ...and it uses even more letters

269 The 'sixth sick sheik's sixth sheep's sick' is the toughest tongue-twister in the English language.

The sixth sick sheik's sixth.... The sick sheik.... The sixth sick... Ahhrr these rotten tongue twisters! What I'm trying to say is... THIS SHEEP'S SICK! ...OK?

270 Glass is made from sand.

While the other kids took their buckets and spades to the beach...Edward the nerd took his calculator.

271 Eleanor Roosevelt received a telegram from the 1939 World's Fair in New York that used only the power from electric eels.

272 The temperature on the moon can drop by up to 500°F (260°C) at night.

273 More than a thousand new insects are discovered every year.

274 In 1889, the commissioner of the United States Patent Office announced that 'Everything that can be invented, has been invented'.

275 A cross between a goat and a sheep is called a 'geep'.

276 Thomas Edison was afraid of the dark.

Maybe Thomas Edison invented the light bulb because he was afraid of the dark.

277 Arecibo observatory in Puerto Rico has one of the largest radio telescopes in the world. It is over 1000 ft (300 m) across and could pick up the signal from a mobile phone on Jupiter.

Freaky Facts

278 Florence Nightingale did not believe in bacteria.

279 Sir Isaac Newton invented the cat flap.

280 Honey is sometimes used in antifreeze mixtures and in the center of golf balls.

281 The Eiffel Tower always leans away from the sun because heat makes the metal expand.

282 The first stethoscope was made in 1816 with a roll of paper.

283 Cat urine glows under a black light.

284 Hot water freezes more quickly than cold water.

285 Every person has a unique tongue print.

286 Your right lung takes in more air than your left lung does.

287 A woman's heart beats faster than a man's.

288 Albert Einstein never wore socks.

289 Astronauts get taller when they are in space.

290 People photocopying their butts is the cause of 23 per cent of all photocopier malfunctions.

291 It is impossible to cry in space because of the lack of gravity.

292 Only one per cent of bacteria are harmful to humans.

293 In Brazil in 1946, a woman gave birth to decaplets (ten children). She had eight girls and two boys.

294 To be a NASA astronaut your height cannot exceed 6 ft (182 cm).

295 Wedding rings are worn on the fourth finger of the left hand because people used to believe that the vein in this finger goes directly to the heart.

296 The average human dream lasts two to three seconds.

297 Albert Einstein's eyes were auctioned in 1994 after being stored in a safety deposit box since his death in 1955.

298 The number of births in India each year exceeds the entire population of Australia (20 million).

299 Every year 4000 people injure themselves with teapots.

300 The measurement from your wrist to your elbow is the same measurement as your foot.

301 Arteries carry blood away from the heart. Veins carry blood towards the heart.

302 According to a study by the Economic Research Service, 27 per cent of all food produced in Western nations ends up in garbage bins. Yet 1.2 billion people in the world are underfed.

303 Girls have more taste buds than boys do.

304 You breathe in and out about 23 000 times a day.

305 One out of twenty people has an extra rib.

306 New Zealand was the first country to give women the vote.

307 The average person has at least seven dreams a night.

308 A corpse left out in warm weather will be reduced to a skeleton in about nine days.

309 The most common name in the world is Mohammed.

310 In India, people wear masks on the back of their heads when they go outside. This confuses tigers because they like to attack from the rear.

311 The Beijing Duck Restaurant in China can seat 9000 people.

312 Color blindness is ten times more common in men than in women.

313 Humans spend a third of their lives sleeping.

314 The Mbuti Pygmies are among the shortest people in the world. The average height for a man is 4 ft 6 in. (137 cm) tall.

315 Lack of sleep will kill a person faster than starvation will.

316 Tibetans and Mongolians put salt in their tea instead of sugar.

317 Your tongue is the strongest muscle in your body.

318 Even the cleverest person only uses one per cent of the English language.

319 Men sweat 40 per cent more than women do.

I feel as fresh as a daisy! Hardly a drop of sweat anywhere!

I feel about as fresh as an old wet gym towel... soaking in sweat... lying on the washroom floor myself!

320 The average person laughs 15 times a day.

321 The largest cell in the human body is the ovum, the female reproductive cell.

322 During your life, you will eat an average of 70 insects and ten spiders while sleeping.

323 Japanese speakers learn Spanish faster than they learn English. English speakers learn Spanish faster than they learn Japanese.

324 The most productive mother gave birth to 69 children.

325 In Albania, nodding your head means no and shaking it means yes.

326 While you are reading this sentence, 50 000 cells in your body will have been replaced by new cells.

327 Although an extremely rare occurrence, sneezing too hard can fracture a rib.

328 Babies are born without kneecaps. Kneecaps do not appear until a child is two years old.

329 The oldest known person lived to 122 years of age.

Cecil leaves the bedroom window open and swallows most of his expected life's quota of 70 insects and ten spiders while he sleeps

Bob...known to his friends at the nursing home as Methusela 'tries to blow and make a wish... But can't get close enough to the cake for the raging inferno created by the 120 birthday candles.

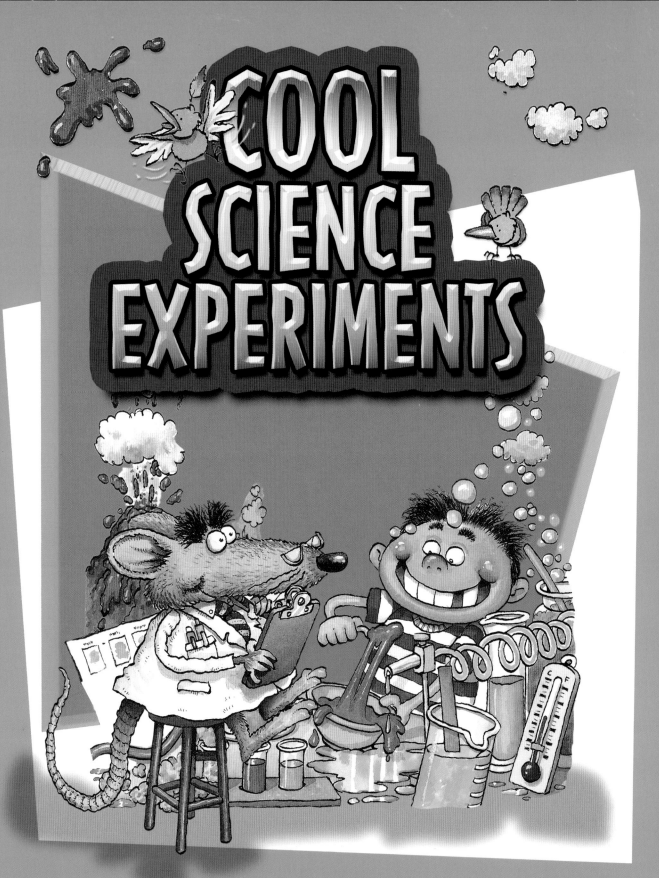

COOL SCIENCE EXPERIMENTS

Even simple science experiments can shock and amaze. Ordinary materials like vinegar, string, eggs, and paper can be used to make extraordinary things. How does gravity work? Will a feather fall faster than a brick? Can a potato dodge obstacles? Can you eat a science experiment?

Find all these answers and more with these wild and wacky science experiments that will help you discover how the world works and why things happen the way they do. Most of all, though, these experiments are fun!

Experiment Rating

Easy	Medium	Difficult	Adult needed
			+ 

Contents

Rat's Rating

Can an egg bounce without breaking? Wait!
Don't try it yet. Read what to do first.

You will need
eggs, water, vinegar,
flashlight, bowl

Rat's Helpful Hint
Don't do this experiment in a hot bath.
The eggs will cook and get hard-boiled.
Also, don't try this at the end of the
week —eggs hate Fry-days.

That's the first time I've ever seen an egg ride a pogo stick!

Anything's possible in Science I suppose!

What to do for this biology experiment

1 Put 1 whole raw egg in a glass of water.

2 Put 1 whole raw egg in a glass of vinegar.

3 The eggs are the same aren't they? Now, leave them for a few hours.

4 Look at both eggs. Do they still look the same? The egg in the water is the same, but the egg in the vinegar has changed. The shell has begun to fizz. The acid in the vinegar dissolves the calcium carbonate that's in the shell.

5 Look carefully. Does the egg in vinegar still have its shell? Touch it. It now feels and looks like a rubber ball, doesn't it?

Hey! Go easy!

6 Leave both eggs alone for 7 days. After that time, take the egg in vinegar to a dark room and shine a flashlight at it. What do you see? The light bounces off the egg, doesn't it?

7 Take the egg out of the glass of vinegar. Hold the egg a little bit over a bowl.

8 Let the egg drop. Do you think it will splatter? Try it!

BOING!

What Happens
Your egg bounces! Try it again getting a little higher each time. See how high you can make the egg bounce. What do you think will happen if you try to bounce the egg that was in the water? Hold it over the bowl and try.

Why
• A chemical change takes place in the egg when left in vinegar.
• The vinegar, which is an acid, reacts with the calcium carbonate of the eggshell.
• The change makes the shell go soft, then disappear. This is called "decalcification".
• The egg in the glass of water does not chemically change.

Fun Fact
You can make chicken bones so soft that you can bend them. Put a clean wishbone or leg bone into a jar of vinegar. Make sure the bones are completely covered. Leave them there for seven days. The bones will go so soft that you can twist them into a knot! Minerals in the bone make it strong and rigid. The vinegar takes away these minerals and the bones dissolve like the eggshell.

Grow a Stalactite

Rat's Rating

Have you ever been in a cave and seen amazing columns? These are stalactites and stalagmites. It takes many hundreds of years for these to grow. You can make your own in just a few weeks!

You will need
glass jars, baking soda or Epsom salts. The salts take longer, but give you more shapes. Spoon, wool/cotton/string — any thread that will soak up water, paperclips, water, saucer

Rat's Helpful Hint
If you get a chance to visit a dark cave, remember to hide around a corner. When someone passes by, leap out and shout "Boo!" Adults just love this!

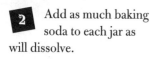

What to do for this chemistry experiment

1 Fill two clean jars with hot water.

2 Add as much baking soda to each jar as will dissolve.

3 Mix well so that the soda is dissolved completely.

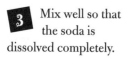

4 Dip each end of the thread into the jars. The ends must be weighed down with paperclips, pencils, popsicle sticks, or nails to keep them in the jars.

5 Place a saucer between the jars to catch the drips.

6 Let the thread hang between the jars and over the saucer.

7 Leave the jars for 2–3 weeks. Will anything grow?

What Happens
A white stalactite grows down from the wool and a stalagmite grows up from the saucer.

Why
• The baking soda mix is carried up through the thread. This is called *capillary action*.
• The mix then drips onto the saucer.
• Over the days, the dripping water evaporates. It leaves a little of the baking soda behind.
• These bits of baking soda make a tiny stalactite and stalagmite.
• After months, these join. They make a single column like the one you see in a cave.

Fun Fact
One of the world's tallest stalagmites is in Slovakia. Cavers found the 106.9 feet (32.6 meters) tall stalagmite in 1964.

Rat's Rating

Like all plants, potatoes turn energy from the sun into food energy to help them live. But what happens if you block out most of the light with obstacles? Are potatoes smart enough to get past your obstacles and reach the light?

You will need
shoe box with lid, a sprouting potato—one with little white shoots growing out of it—scissors, potting soil, 'obstacles' such as small boxes, cotton reels, baby food jars, sunny days

What to do for this biology experiment

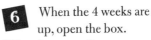

1 Cut a small coin size gap in the short side of the box.

2 Put a handful of the potting soil in the corner of the shoebox. It must be at the opposite end from the hole you made.

3 Lay the potato on the soil.

4 Put the 'obstacles' in the box. The smaller the box, the less obstacles you will need.

5 Put the lid on. Place the box anywhere that gets lots of sun. Don't touch the box for 4 weeks.

6 When the 4 weeks are up, open the box. What do you see?

Hmmm A nice and comfy piece of dirt

AHHRR MY EYES!

SHOES

What Happens
The shoot has made its way over or around the obstacles you left in the way and has reached the hole.

Why
• Plants have cells. These are sensitive to light. The cells show the plant which way to grow.
• A tiny bit of light came into the shoebox. The potato shoot twisted until it reached the light.
• Plants will always grow towards the light, even if they are buried deep in the soil.
• The shoot should be green, but it's white. This is because the *chlorophyll* that makes it green can't be made in the dark shoebox.

Fun Fact
In France, potato chips have been popular since the 1700s! It was the invention of the mechanical potato peeler in the 1920s that made potato chips go from a small specialty item to a top selling snack food.

If I could only invent the POTATO CHIP... I could be a wealthy man! I could even be a millionaire!! But I'd need to peel faster...

Wait and See

Fuzz Balls

Rat's Rating

Can mold be useful in making medicine? Does bacteria have an infectious laugh? Let's find out.

I don't like the way that mold is staring at me!

You will need
oranges, lemons, or other citrus fruits, bowl, clear polythene bags (the type bread comes in), cotton balls

Rat's Helpful Hint
If you don't have time to do this experiment, just look behind the sofa, or under your bed. You're sure to find all sorts of moldy food.

What to do for this botany experiment

1 Place the fruit in a bowl. Leave it out in the air for 1 day.

2 Open the 2 bread bags. Put 1 orange, 1 lemon, and a wet cotton ball in each bag.

3 Tie the ends of the bags.

4 Place one bag in the refrigerator.

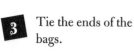

5 Place the other bag in a warm dark place.

6 Leave the bags closed for 2 weeks.

7 Check the fruit through the bags each day.

EEEEE… That's some mighty ugly citrus fruit!

What Happens
The fruit in the refrigerator stays much the same. At worst, it may be a bit drier. The other fruit has turned into blue-green fuzz balls. This fuzzy growth on the outside of the fruit is *penicillin*.

Why
• Mold is a form of fungus that makes tiny cells called *spores*.
• Spores are even tinier than dust particles! They float through the air.
• Mold grows faster in moist warm places. That is why foods become moldier in the summer.
• Keeping food cool slows the growth of mold. Freezing keeps foods fresh for even longer periods.
• Fungi are all around us. They usually don't reach the fruiting body stage. This is because there aren't enough nutrients and water available.

You gotta see this! There's more than PENICILLIN living in your toothbrush! Where's it been?

In my MOUTH…

Fun Facts
Under a microscope, penicillin mold looks like a small brush. The Latin word for paintbrush is 'penicillus'. This is how penicillin got its name. The word pencil also comes from this Latin word, because brushes were used for writing.

Experiment

5

Rat's Rating

Can something be a solid and a liquid at the same time? Sounds impossible! What do you think?

I may look like an uninteresting glob of corn starch...but I can do some amazing things!

You will need

cornstarch, measuring cup, mixing spoon, bowl

What to do for this chemistry experiment

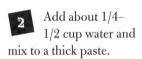

1 Place 1 cup of cornstarch in a large bowl.

2 Add about 1/4–1/2 cup water and mix to a thick paste.

3 The powder is solid. The water is a liquid. Do you think the mixture will be a solid or a liquid?

4 Actually, it's both! With your hands, knead a handful of the mixture. It will become firm as long as you keep kneading.

5 Stop kneading. Quickly punch the mixture with your fist. It feels hard and may even crack.

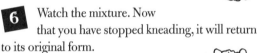

6 Watch the mixture. Now that you have stopped kneading, it will return to its original form.

7 Push your fingers into it very slowly. They will slide in as though the mixture is a liquid. Raise your hands and see it pour through your fingers.

What Happens
As it stands, the mixture is a liquid—it's just water with powder floating in it. However, when you hit it, the water molecules are forced into the middle of each grain of powder, so the mixture is solid.

Does your water taste a little... Prehistoric? *Sure does! A little Jurassic actually!*

👉 Fun Fact
Do you know that when you drink water you're drinking dinosaur spit? The water we have today is the same water that the dinosaurs drank. How can this be? Well, it can take a water molecule thousands of years to finish a cycle from ocean to sky to land and back to the ocean again. This is because the water may be trapped in ice for a very long time.

Why
- Some fluid mixtures have two forms.
- *Isotropy* is when a liquid becomes solid when moved.
- You can see this when walking on wet sand. The sand firms up below your feet when you first walk. It then becomes more liquid as your feet sink into it a moment later. If you run over the sand, it will feel hard. If you walk slowly, your feet will sink below the surface with each step.
- *Thixotropy* is the opposite of *isotropy*. *Thixotropy* is when the liquid mixture becomes more liquid as it is moved.
- You might have done this when you hit the end of a ketchup bottle to get the ketchup to come out. The force temporarily makes the ketchup 'runny' and it comes out easily from the bottle.

Fizzy, Flowing, and Funky

Invisible Ink

Rat's Rating

You've heard of secret messages written in code, haven't you? But have you heard of secret messages being written with invisible ink?

"PAINTING IN INVISIBLE INK" by I.C. LITTLE

You will need
lemon, saucer, water, teaspoon, toothpick, white paper, lamp

Rat's Helpful Hint
Why not send your invisible ink letter to a friend to read?

What to do for this chemistry experiment

1 Squeeze the lemon juice into the saucer.

2 Add a few drops of water and mix well with the spoon.

3 Dip the toothpick into the lemon juice mix. Not too much or you'll make invisible blobs!

4 Use the toothpick to write a message on ordinary white paper. Thick paper works best.

5 When it dries, the writing will be invisible.

6 Heat the paper by holding it with the written side down near a light bulb. If an adult is helping, you can use heat from a stove or candle. What do you see?

What Happens
While it heats up, the invisible ink writing slowly becomes brown and visible. The words appear on the page.

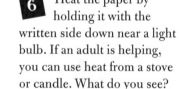

Why
• The juice of lemons has compounds of *carbon*.
• These compounds have almost no color when you dissolve them in water.
• When you heat them, the carbon compounds break down and turn black.

This message is no longer a SECRET!

Fun Fact
Batteries have a chemical called an *electrolyte*. An electrolyte lets a chemical reaction take place between the electrodes. The reaction makes electricity. In this experiment, lemon juice acts as an electrolyte.

My old lemons were flat in my flashlight... So I'm installing fresh ones

7

Rat's Rating

Have you seen a real volcano erupt? Well, make your own.
It's much safer.

You will need
flour, salt, cooking oil, water, large bowl,
clean plastic soda bottle, baking pan,
food coloring—red looks good—liquid
detergent, baking soda, vinegar, water

Rat's Helpful Hint
This is a messy experiment. Make
sure you know who's going to be
cleaning up. Don't let your dog be
the one to lick up the mess.

OOHH! That must have been
a terrible headache!

What to do in this chemistry experiment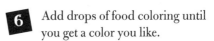

1 Mix 6 cups of flour, 2 cups of salt, 4 tablespoons of cooking oil, and 2 cups of water in a large bowl.

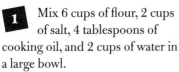

2 Using your hands, mix the ingredients until smooth and firm. Add more water to the mixture if needed.

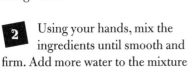

3 Stand the soda bottle in the baking pan.

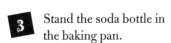

4 Mold the salt dough around the bottle. Make sure you don't cover up the bottle mouth or drop any dough in the bottle. You can build your volcano with as much detail as you like, or leave it plain.

5 Fill the bottle almost to the top with warm water.

6 Add drops of food coloring until you get a color you like.

7 Squeeze 6 drops of the liquid detergent into the bottle.

8 Add 2 tablespoons of baking soda.

9 Slowly pour vinegar into the bottle and jump back quickly. What do you think will happen?

What Happens
The 'lava' flows out of your volcano.

Why
• Mixing baking soda and vinegar makes a chemical reaction.
• A chemical reaction is where one substance is chemically changed to another.
• All chemical reactions are about the making or destroying of bonds between atoms in which carbon dioxide gas is made—the same gas that bubbles in a real volcano.
• The gas bubbles build up in the bottle. They force the liquid 'lava' mixture up and over the mouth of your volcano.

VESUVIUS erupting NOW!

Fun Fact
Over the long term, volcanic eruptions can help us. Volcanic materials break down and weather so that they form fertile soils.

71

Fizzy, Flowing, and Funky

On Your Mark - Go!

Rat's Rating

You've heard of horse racing and car racing, but did you know that marker pens could race each other?

You will need
4 different brands of black markers, white coffee filter paper/ paper towels, clear drinking glass, pencil, clothes pins

IF I were a GAMBLING RAT and not a LAB RAT. My money would be on this speedy looking black pen over here!

What to do in this biology experiment

1 Cut a rectangle out of the coffee filter. The width of the paper must fit easily in the glass. But the top of the filter paper must stick out!

2 Using a pencil, draw a line about 1 inch (2.5 cm) up from the bottom of the filter paper.

3 Using each black marker place a small dot along the line. Don't put the dots too close together.

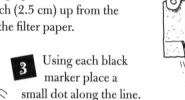

4 Put the filter paper in the glass.

5 Clip the clothes pins to the paper. Rest the clothes pins across the top of the glass to stop the paper from slipping down.

6 Adjust the clothes pins so the filter paper just touches the bottom of the glass.

7 Lift the filter paper out without unclipping the clothes pins. Put it to one side.

8 Put a 1/4 inch (.05 cm) of water in the glass.

9 Put the glass in a place where it won't be bumped.

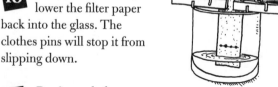

10 Slowly and carefully, lower the filter paper back into the glass. The clothes pins will stop it from slipping down.

11 Don't touch the experiment, or it will go crazy!

12 Wait 5 minutes and see what has happened. Check again in another 5 minutes. Do you think the different black dots will do different things?

13 Once any changes have stopped, take the filter paper out of the glass or it will ruin the experiment.

Why
• Most black markers are made from colored pigments or dyes and water.
• The water in the ink carries the pigments up the filter paper.
• As the water dries, the pigments stay on the paper.
• The pigments dissolve when the filter is dipped in water.
• Some pigments move up the paper faster than others. They travel at different speeds. This depends on how large the pigment molecule is and how much the pigment is attracted to the paper.

What Happens
You will start to see different colors. Some of the markers might reach the top faster than others, or some might be more colorful. It all depends on what pens you use.

Rat's Rating

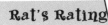

Want to wrap a small gift but don't have any wrapping paper? Try making your own by using ordinary sheets of white paper. Here's how.

You will need

colored chalk—go for colors that will look good together, white paper—amount depends on how much swirly paper you want to make, paper or plastic cups, rolling pin, vinegar, zip lock plastic bags, plastic spoon, large plastic bowl, newspaper, water, cooking oil

What to do in this chemistry experiment

1 Place sheets of newspaper on a table.

2 Fill the bowl with water.

3 Add 2 tablespoons of vinegar.

4 Place the bowl in the center of the newspaper.

5 Place small pieces of different colored chalk into separate zip lock up bag. Zip up the bag.

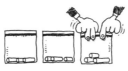

6 Use the rolling pin to crush the chalk into a fine powder.

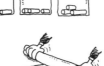

7 Tip each powdered chalk color into its own cup.

8 Pour 1 tablespoon of oil into each cup. Stir well with the plastic spoon.

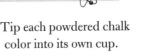

9 Pour the contents of each cup into the bowl of water. The chalky colored oil should form large colored pools on top of the water.

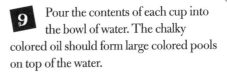

10 Carefully lay each piece of white paper on the surface of the water.

11 Lift out and place on the sheets of newspaper to dry. This will take about 24 hours.

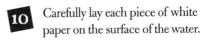

12 When the papers are fully dried, carefully wipe off any surface chalk grains with a paper towel. What do you have left?

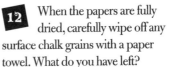

What Happens

The colored oil sticks to the paper and makes swirls and streaky patterns.

Why

• Negative and positive charged molecules are attracted to each other.
• The molecules of chalk (calcium carbonate) and vinegar (acetic acid) and water and the surface of the paper all chemically mix to make a chemical bond.
• This causes the streaky colors to stick to the paper.

Fun Fact

A film of oil on water will kill mosquito larvae. This is because the oil clogs up the snorkel that the larvae use to breathe.

WOH! TAKE A DEEP BREATH GUYS! Someone up there is making that STREAKY PAPER BIRTHDAY WRAP!!

Experiment 10 — Twister

WHOA! What have I created? A TWISTER? Oh... It's only a Mobius strip!

Can there ever be a place where inside and outside is one and the same?

You will need
sheet of paper, scissors, pen, masking tape

What to do in this topology experiment

1 Cut the paper into a long rectangle about 1 inch (2 cm) wide.

2 Hold the strip out straight.

3 Give it a half twist (180 degrees). Use the masking tape to stick the two ends together.

4 Hold the edge of the strip against the tip of a pen.

5 Draw a line down the center of the strip. Don't take the pen off the paper.

6 Turn the paper and keep on drawing the line. You will move the paper as you go along. Do not stop until your line meets up with your starting point.

7 Take off the masking tape. Look at the paper. What have you done?

What Happens
You have drawn on both sides of the paper without lifting your pen! Now, tape it back how it was before (with a half twist). With the scissors, cut the strip along the center line that you drew. Can you guess what you will make? You have made a chain that is twice as long as your original loop!

Why
• Your shape is known as a Mobius strip.
• When you twisted your strip, the inside and outside became one continuous surface.
• When you cut the strip, it became one longer chain. But it still had only one continuous surface.
• Now, try the experiment again. This time give the paper a full twist. You'll be surprised at what you see.

Fun Fact
During the early 1800s, the German mathematician August Mobius helped develop a study in geometry that is known as *topology*. Topology explores the properties of geometrical figures that do not change when the figure is bent, or stretched.

I don't know what I'm making! I was going to call it a MOBIUS STRIP... But I think I'll just call it .... a mess!

11

Rat's Rating

Here is your chance to make all the noise you want—and you can blame it all on science.

AHHRR... My favorite OBOE CONCERTO!

We hope that you enjoyed this live performance of the DRINKING STRAW CONCERTO in G MINOR

It sounded like an OBOE to me!

Rat's Helpful Hints

Try this early on a Sunday morning when the rest of the house is asleep. The best way to do it is to stand by a bedroom door. Be careful though, sound bytes bite, so maybe you really shouldn't!

You will need
drinking straw, scissors

What to do in this sound experiment

1 Pinch flat 1/2 inch to 3/4 inch (12–19 mm) of one end of the straw.

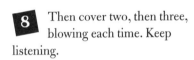

2 Cut off little triangles. These make the reeds.

3 Put the straw far enough into your mouth so your lips do not touch the corners.

4 Press with your lips on the straw, but not too hard. Blow gently just past the cut. Listen to the sound. Keep trying. It may take a few tries.

5 Cut three small slits along the length of the straw about 1 inch (2.5 cm) apart.

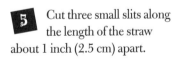

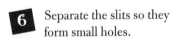

6 Separate the slits so they form small holes.

7 Cover one of them and blow as before.

8 Then cover two, then three, blowing each time. Keep listening.

Fun Fact

Another way to be heard is with a piece of cellophane 2 inches (5 cm) square. Stretch it tightly between the thumbs and index fingers of both hands. Hold your hands in front of your face so the cellophane is in front of your lips. Blow hard and fast at the edge of the tightly stretched piece of cellophane. Keep your lips close together. You must send a thin stream of air right at the edge of the cellophane.

Can you hear a noise? When the air hits the edge of the cellophane, you'll make a scream. If you don't, change the distance between the cellophane and your lips until the air hits it just right. The fast-moving air from your lip makes the edges of the cellophane vibrate. Because the cellophane is very thin, the jet of air makes these vibrations very fast. The faster something vibrates the higher the tone it creates.

Why
• As in a real oboe, the reeds open and close at high speed.
• This first allows air to flow into the straw and then to stop the flow.
• Vibrating air makes the sound.
• As you cover and uncover the holes, you regulate the length of the air column. That decides the pitch.
• The shorter the air column, the faster it vibrates and the higher the note.

What Happens
Each time you blow, you hear a different sound. You can play simple tunes by covering and uncovering the holes.

Candle in the Wind

12

What is the connection between a candle experiment and the shape of a bird and airplane wing? Find out.

You will need

a candle, low candle holder, cylinder-shaped container the same height as the candle—a metal or ceramic salt shaker is perfect, ADULT SUPERVISION

What to do in this forces experiment

1 Ask an adult to light a candle. Put it in a low holder and place it on the table.

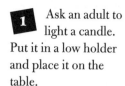

2 Stand a salt container 3 inches (8 cm) in front of the candle.

3 Stand on the opposite side of the lit candle. Blow against the container. Make sure you keep your mouth even with the flame of the candle. Do you think you can blow out the candle? Of course not! The container's in the way. Or is it?

What Happens

The candle goes out!

Why

• Air follows the curved shape of the container.
• When the streams of air meet on the other side, they join to blow out the candle.

Fun Fact

You can make your own aerofoil. You'll need a piece of thin cardboard 6 in. × 9 in. (16 cm × 23 cm), tape, a pen, a drinking straw 2 in. (5 cm) long, and a piece of string 39 in. (100 cm). Fold the card in two, leaving an overlap of 1/3 inch (1 cm). Push the overlapping ends together. This makes one side of the folded paper curve. Tape the ends together. Use a pen to make a hole through the middle of the wing. Carefully push a drinking straw through the hole. Thread the string through the straw. Pull the two ends of the string tight, holding one in each hand. Check the wing has the curved surface upwards and the wider surface is facing forwards. Keep holding the string tightly. Quickly run forward. Your aerofoil will move up the string.

Can a ball float on an invisible stream of air?

You will need
a hair dryer, ping-pong ball/round balloon/
Styrofoam ball, tissue

What to do in this physics experiment

1 Turn on the hair dryer.

2 Blow a stream of air straight up.

3 Carefully balance the ping-pong ball above the stream of air.

4 Pull it slowly out of the stream. What do you see? When only half the ball is out of the stream of air, you can feel it being sucked back.

5 Let go of the ball. It will waver back and forth and then settle near the center of the stream of air.

What Happens
The ping-pong ball floats freely in the air. When you try to pull the ball out of the stream of air, you can feel a force pulling it back in. You can feel the ball turning the stream.

6 Keep the ball a little way out of the stream of air. With the other hand, dangle a tissue and look for the stream of air above the ball. See how the ball turns the stream outward.

7 Tilt the stream of air to one side and see how the ball is still hanging.

8 Balance the ball in the stream of air.

9 Move the hair dryer and the ball toward the corner of a room. Look at how much higher the hanging ball moves.

Why
• When the ball is hanging in the stream of air, the air flowing up hits the bottom of the ball.
• It slows and makes an area of higher pressure.
• The high pressure area of air under the ball holds the ball up against the pull of gravity.
• When you pull the ball a little bit out of the stream, the air flows around the curve of the ball that is nearest the center of the stream of air.
• Air rushes in an arc around the top of the ball. It then moves out above the ball.
• This outward flowing air puts out an inward force on the ball.

Fun Fact
The downward flow of air under a helicopter puts an upward force on the blades. The blades create lift by deflecting air downward.

Hot Stuff

Hot Diggity Dog

YUM! THERE'S NOTHING LIKE... ......an empty pizza box!

14

Rat's Rating

Solar energy can change directly or indirectly into other forms of energy, such as heat and electricity. But can you cook with it? Make a solar oven and find out.

You will need
a very hot sunny day, pizza box, black construction paper, wide aluminum foil, sheet of plastic, glue, tape, scissors, ruler, marker, string, nail, skewer, choice of food to cook—hot dogs/pancakes

What to do in this heat experiment

1 Tape the foil to the inside bottom of the clean pizza box.

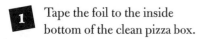

2 Cover the foil with the black paper. Tape it down.

3 Put the box on the sheet of plastic.

4 Draw the outline of the box on the plastic with the marker.

5 Cut the plastic about 1/4 inch (0.5 cm) inside the marks.

CUT 0.5cm in from PEN LINE

6 On the top of the box, draw a line 1 inch (10 cm) from all sides.

7 Cut along the front and side lines. Do not cut along the back. This will be the hinge for the flap. Carefully fold open the flap.

8 Cut a piece of foil the same size as the flap. Glue it to the side of the flap that faces into the box. Flatten out any wrinkles.

FOIL

9 Wipe any glue off with a damp towel before it dries.

TAPE PLASTIC ON HERE   FOIL

10 Tape the plastic to the inside of the box. Make it tight so it looks like glass.

11 Tape the other edges. Make sure it is tight so no air can get in.

12 Cut a piece of string as long as the box. Tape one end to the top of the flap.

13 Push a small nail into the back of the box so you have a place to tie the string.

14 Poke a metal skewer through the middle of your hot dog. It will cook more quickly if cut in half.

15 Put the hot dog in your solar oven. Place the oven in a hot spot. The sun needs to shine right into the box. The best time to use your solar oven is between 12 and 2.00 p.m. This is when the sun is at its strongest.

SIZZLE SIZZLE SIZZLE

COOKED FOOD!

What Happens
Your food will cook, but it can take many hours.

Why
• Your hot dog oven is a solar collector. Sunlight hits the reflective foil surface. It focuses on the hot dog held in the center.

Rat's Rating

This one is to see how a thermometer works—just for fun.

You will need

clear medicine bottle or very small jar, clear drinking straw or medicine dropper tube, cold water, spoon, food coloring, modeling clay/plasticine, marker, note book paper

What to do for this temperature experiment

The things a rat will do for science...

1 Pour cold water into the medicine bottle. Fill to about 1/4 full.

2 Add a couple of drops of food coloring.

3 Get a wad of modeling clay. Push the straw through it. Unclog the straw if bits of clay end up in it.

4 Put the straw in the bottle. Make sure it doesn't touch the bottom.

5 Work the modeling clay to seal the neck of the bottle. The straw needs to stay in place.

6 Blow gently into the straw so the water rises. When it is halfway up the straw stop blowing.

7 Use your marker to make a line where the water has risen on the straw.

8 Write down the height of the water in the straw. This will be the height at room temperature.

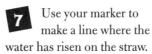

9 Hold your hands on the bottle. Watch what happens to the height of the mixture in the bottle.

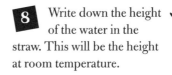

10 Mark the new level with a different color pen.

What Happens
The height of the mixture rises.

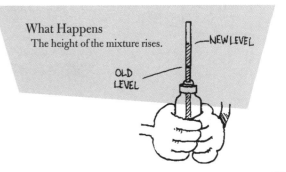

NEW LEVEL

OLD LEVEL

Why
• Just like any thermometer, the mixture expands when it becomes warm. This means the liquid no longer fits in the bottom of the bottle.
• As the water expands, the colored mixture moves up through the straw.

Fun Fact
The Italian physicist Galileo invented the first thermometer 1593.

Mama-Mia it's-a hot in-a here! I should invent-a a THERMOMETER to see-a how hot it is! It's-a like living in-a the tropics!

The Drip

Experiment 16

Which runs faster, hot or cold water? Hot runs faster because you can't catch a hot, but you can catch a cold!

You will need
paper cups, pins, small drinking glass, water, ice-cubes

What to do in this temperature experiment

1 In the middle of the bottom of 2 paper cups make a tiny pinhole. Make sure they are the same size.

2 Stand the paper cups on top of the glasses.

3 Pour very cold water into 1 glass until it's 1/2 full.

4 Add a few ice-cubes to make sure it is really cold.

5 Pour hot water into the other glass until it is also 1/2 full. Watch as water drips from the paper cups into the glasses. Do you see any differences?

Fun Fact
You can see molecules with the help of food coloring. Get 2 drinking glasses that are exactly the same. Put 1/2 cup of water in each of them. One glass should have cold tap water and the other hot tap water. Put 2 drops of food coloring in each glass. Time how long it takes for each of the colors to spread in the water. Molecules make the colors spread.

What Happens
If the holes are the same size, you'll see that the hot water leaks faster than the cold water. If the cold water is cold enough, it may not leak at all.

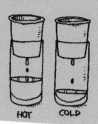

Why
• Molecules exist although we can't see them.
• The molecules in hot water move faster than in cold water.
• The faster they move, the easier it is for them to slip past each other. That is why hot water is more likely to leak than cold.

Pop Goes the Popcorn
Experiment 17

Rat's Rating

Why does popcorn pop? Grab an adult to help you find out. This experiment is hot!

You will need
unpopped popcorn, a medium pan with a clear lid, at least enough popcorn to cover the bottom of the pan, one kernel deep, 1/3 cup of oil for every cup of kernels (don't use butter), stove

What to do in this temperature experiment

1 Put the oil into the pan.

2 Place the pan on the stove.

3 Ask an adult to heat the oil so that it is very hot (if the oil smokes, it is too hot).

4 Test the oil on a couple of kernels. When they pop, add the rest of the corn.

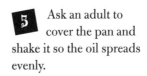

5 Ask an adult to cover the pan and shake it so the oil spreads evenly.

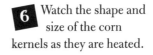

6 Watch the shape and size of the corn kernels as they are heated.

7 When the popping begins to slow, ask an adult to take the pan away from the stovetop. The heated oil will still pop the rest of the kernels.

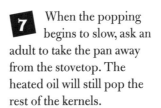

What Happens
The corn kernels change from small, hard, orange kernels to big, soft, white shapes.

Fun Fact
The largest box of popcorn in the world was made in London in 2000. The box was 6 × 6 × 12 feet (1.8 × 1.8 × 3.6 meters) and filled with 784 square feet (22.2 square meters) of popcorn. It took 5 hours to fill.

Why
• The tough outside of the unpopped kernel is the *pericarp*. This is the part that often gets stuck between your teeth when you eat popcorn.
• The inside is full of starch. This grows into the white fluffy popcorn.
• The small amount of water inside the kernel makes this happen. As the kernel is heated, the water evaporates. It changes to a gas. The gas grows and pushes hard on the pericarp. It breaks and the starch tissue inside is blown outward.
• The popping noise is the sound of steam escaping and the pericarp breaking.

Too Twisty Too Twirly

Rat's Rating

How much power do you have in your hot little hands? Find out.

> **You will need**
> adult supervision, thin sheet of paper, pin, pencil with eraser

What to do in this temperature experiment

1 Cut your thin paper into a 3 × 3 inches (7.5 × 7.5 cm) square.

2 Fold the square diagonally one way and then unfold it.

3 Fold the square diagonally the other way.

4 Push in gently on opposite sides of the paper. This makes the center rise about 1/2 inch (1.25 cm) higher than the sides.

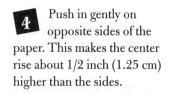

5 Push the straight pin into the eraser end of the pencil. Leave 1 inch (2.5 cm) of the pin sticking straight up.

6 Sit down and hold the pencil between your knees.

7 Set the paper square on top of the pencil. You must have the head of the pin right at the center peak where the two folds come together.

8 Cup your hands on each side of the paper. They must be about 1 inch (2.5 cm) away from it.

9 Do not move your hands or knees. Wait a minute and watch what happens to the paper.

Fun Fact
Hot-air balloons don't fly in the rain. This is because balloon heat can cause water to boil on top of the balloon and boiling water destroys the canopy fabric.

What Happens
Your paper twirler will begin to turn. Once it gets going your twirler will twirl around and around.

Why
• The warmth from your hands heats the air around them.
• The heated air rises.
• The rising air makes the finely balanced twirler twirl.

It's Raining Cats and Dogs

Experiment

19

Rat's Rating

Fed up with having to water the potted plants? Bring them inside while you do this experiment. You're going to make it rain in your kitchen.

You will need
saucepan, water, ice-cubes, tray, potholder/oven mitts, an adult's supervision

What to do in this meteorology experiment

1 Put water in the saucepan.

3 Hold a tray of ice-cubes above the steam. Use potholders to protect your hands.

2 Ask an adult to boil the water until steam rises.

4 Keep holding the tray until drops form on the bottom.

What Happens
The drops of water grow heavy and fall like rain.

Why
• The cold surfaces of the ice-cube tray cool the steam from the boiling water.
• The steam changes back into water, and collects in drops.
• As the drops get bigger and heavier, it rains.
• The boiling water is like the water that evaporates into the air as water vapor.
• As the vapor rises, it cools. You see clouds when droplets form. As these droplets collect more moisture, they become heavy enough to fall to earth as rain.

Fun Fact
If you hold a piece of cardboard outside when it starts to rain you can measure the size of a raindrop. A downpour has about 113 drops.

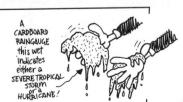

A CARDBOARD RAINGAUGE this wet indicates either a SEVERE TROPICAL STORM or a HURRICANE!

Eat Your Science

Cheese Fractures

Experiment

20

You will need
pre-sliced manufactured cheese (the smooth type that comes individually wrapped in plastic)

Rat's Rating

Grab slices of cheese and learn how fractures, breaks, and cracks grow.

1 Take a slice of cheese and pull on the edges. Does it tear apart? Good, now eat it.

2 Get another cheese slice. Use your fingernail to make a cut parallel to the edge of the cheese slice.

3 Pull on the two cheese edges parallel to the cut. You'll be pulling in a direction at right angles to the cut. Watch how the small fault you've made in the cheese slice concentrates the tearing. Look at the shape of the fracture. It multiplies at the tips where the tearing is taking place. The fracture tips move faster as the fracture gets bigger. Eat the torn up slice.

4 Get another cheese slice. Make two cuts near the middle of the cheese about 1 inch (2.5 cm) apart. Make the cuts so they're balanced diagonally from each other.

5 Pull on the cheese. What happens?

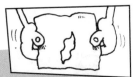

What Happens
You have made tension fractures. This is how things pull apart. The tips of these fractures begin to multiply past each other. They will curve inwards and link up into a single fracture. Like your slice of cheese, basic forces can pull on the crusts of the Earth and other planets. This makes tension fractures. Some of these link together to make bigger faults.

Gumdrop Diamond

Experiment

21

You will need
fruit gums/gumdrops or marshmallows, toothpicks

Rat's Rating

Build a model of a diamond structure that you can eat!

1 Push 3 toothpicks all the way into a fruit gum. They must be in a triangle shape so the fruit gum can stand.

2 Get another fruit gum and pick up another toothpick. Anchor the bottom legs together and start building upward.

3 Keep building the shape. Every time toothpicks come together, anchor them with a fruit gum.

4 Start with a triangle-shaped base of 15 fruit gums with 5 to each side of the triangle.

5 Do you know what you have built?

What Happens
You have built a tetrahedron. It is like a tripod and is a very strong shape. In your model, the gumdrops are like carbon atoms. Toothpicks are bonds between the atoms.

Wave in a Bottle

Experiment

22

Rat's Rating

Want to control a tiny ocean? With this experiment,
you can see how an ocean wave is made and grows larger.
You can have a calm day, or whip up a storm at sea.

You will need
empty soda bottle and cap (or cork to
fit the bottle), vegetable oil, water, food
coloring

Rat's Helpful Hint
Make sure you use a clear bottle or you
won't be able to see anything!

What to do in this forces experiment

1 Wash out the bottle.

2 Take off the label by soaking
the bottle in hot water.

3 Fill the bottle with 3/4 cup
of water.

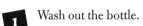

4 Add drops of food coloring.
Stop when you like the color.

5 Pour a 1/4 cup of oil into the bottle.

6 Screw on the cap.

7 Turn the bottle on
its side. Let it settle
for a few minutes. What
happens to the water?

What Happens
The water sinks to the
bottom. There is a clear line
between the colored water
and the oil. Now, tip the bottle
back and forth and make some
waves. Experiment to see what
kind of waves you can make.
See how the waves grow bigger
from one end of the bottle to
the other.

Why
• Your bottle wave is like an ocean
wave.
• Water moves up and down. It
doesn't move forward as the wave
goes through the water.
• The friction between the water and
the wind makes a wave. They move
forward without replacing any water.
• Ordinary ocean waves get their
energy from the wind. Higher waves
need more energy.
• Wind generated ocean waves keep
on traveling after the wind stops.
• Longer waves travel faster than
shorter ones and go farther before
friction makes them disappear.

Fun Facts
Can a rope be like a wave? Yes,
it can! Get a friend to hold one
end of the rope, or tie it to a
tree. When you shake your
end of the rope, waves run
along it. But the rope itself
doesn't move forward. When
an ocean wave reaches land,
however, the wave starts to
drag on the bottom, and the
water begins to move.

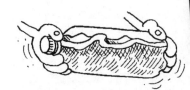

Moving Water

Rat's Rating

Do hot and cold water mix?

You will need

clear jars the same size—baby food jars work well, food coloring—red and blue look good, card to fit over the mouth of your jar, water, sink, a friend

What to do in this water experiment

1 Pour cold water and a few drops of blue coloring into jar 1. Slowly add more water until you see a bulge of water over the rim of the jar.

2 Ask an adult to boil some water. Have them fill jar 2 with hot water.

3 Put a few drops of red food coloring into jar 2.

4 Lay the card carefully onto the top of jar 1.

5 This part is tricky. You may want to do it over a sink! Pick up jar 1. Turn it upside down. Put it over jar 2. You want the card to be flat and make a seal. You don't need to put your hand on the card.

The water will hold it in place. Just flip the jar over. Don't stop for a second! If the jar tilts, but isn't turned over completely, the water will gush out.

6 Keep the necks of the jars close together. Ask a friend to hold onto both jars while you very slowly and carefully pull out the card. What happens? What color is the cold water in the top jar? What color is the hot water in the bottom jar?

7 Empty both jars. Rinse them. Repeat steps 1 through 6, but put the jar with the cold water in the sink and put the card on top of the jar with the red colored hot water. Turn the hot water jar upside down and put it on top of the cold water jar. What happens? What color is the water in the top jar? What color is the water in the bottom jar?

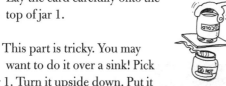

What Happens
The red colored hot water rises into the cold water jar.

HOT (RED) RISES INTO THE BLUE

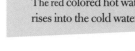

Fun Facts
Would you spend $100 for a glass of water? In America around 1848, people on the way west to the California gold rush did. Because of poor planning, many people weren't ready for the hot, dry deserts of Nevada. A few men in California knew this and traveled east with barrels of water. Very thirsty people paid up to $100 for a glass of precious water.

Why
- Cold water is heavier than hot water.
- The cold water goes down into the bottom jar, pushing the hot water up in small currents.
- When you heat up water, the water molecules start moving around faster and faster. They bounce off each other and move further apart.
- Because there is more space between the molecules, a volume of hot water has fewer molecules in it. It weighs a bit less than the same volume of cold water. So hot water is less dense than cold water.
- When you put the two jars together with the hot water on the bottom, the hot water rises to the top.
- Along the way, it mixes with the cold water and makes purple water.
- When the cold water is on the bottom, the water does not mix. The hot water does not have to rise—it is already on top!

Will Humpty-Dumpty Crack Under Pressure?

Experiment

24

Rat's Rating

Are eggshells fragile? Or do they have super strength? Try this egg-citing egg-speriment to find out.

Now we've got an egg cracking PRESSURE TEST coming up... So... have we got any HUMPTY's in here?

Not me ...I'm GREG

No...I'm BOB!

I'm STEWART!

I'm ROSEMARY!

You will need
eggshell halves, cup, masking tape, fingernail scissors, canned food, piece of cardboard box

Rat's Helpful Hints
Don't ever use reptile eggs. They may hatch into young alligators, snakes or lizards. That would definitely spoil the experiment.

What to do in this forces experiment

1 Wrap a strip of masking tape around the middle of 4 eggshell halves. Keep a gap between the ends of the masking tape.

LEAVE A GAP HERE

2 Carefully make a hole in the eggshell between the gap in the tape.

3 Empty the insides into a cup. Keep the empty eggshells.

4 Put the nail scissors into the hole.

5 Cut around the middle of the eggshell covered with the masking tape.

6 Separate the halves. Trim off any jagged pieces of eggshell. Each one needs a straight-edged bottom.

7 Lay the eggshells, dome-side up, so they make a square.

8 Place the piece of cardboard box on top. Stand a can on top of the cardboard.

What Happens
Did the eggshells crack? Stack another can on top of the first one. Will the eggs crack now? Keep stacking the cans. How many cans are you able to stack before any of the eggs crack? Can you beat our record of 11 cans? How much weight did the eggs hold?

Why
• The strength of the egg is in its dome shape.
• No single point in the dome supports the whole weight of the cans on top of it.
• The weight spreads along the curved walls to the wide base, allowing the eggshell to hold more weight.

 Fun Facts
Can't remember if an egg is raw or hard-boiled? Just spin the egg on its side and hold it for a moment. Let go. If the egg stops, it is hard-boiled. If it keeps spinning, the egg is raw. This is because a raw egg still has liquid inside. When you hold the egg, the liquid keeps turning. When you release the egg, the spinning liquid inside keeps the egg turning.

A Little Pressure

Experiment

25

Who Won? It's a Straw

Rat's Rating

Do you think you can use a straw to pull liquid up into your mouth? No you can't! Find out why.

What's that? You need my STRAW for an experiment? Maybe come back later. I'm enjoying my Lemonade!

You will need
drinking straw, drinking glasses, water

What to do in this forces experiment

1 Half fill one glass with water.

2 Put the straw in the glass. Suck a small amount of water into the straw.

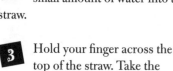

3 Hold your finger across the top of the straw. Take the straw out of the water.

4 Place the straw over the second empty glass.

5 Take your finger away from the top of the straw.

6 Watch the water.

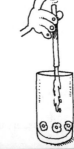

What Happens
The water comes out.

Why
- When you suck through a straw, you don't pull the liquid up. What you're doing is taking away some of the air inside the straw.
- This makes the pressure inside the straw lower than the pressure outside.
- The greater pressure of the outside air then pushes the water in the glass up through the straw and into your mouth.
- When your finger covers the top of the straw, the water stays in the straw.
- It lessens the pressure of the air from above the straw.
- The greater air pressure under the straw holds the water inside it.

I hope one day someone invents the perfect drinking straw...one made out of plastic! I've never been much for the taste of bamboo.

Fun Facts
In 1888, Marvin Stone patented the spiral winding process to make the first paper drinking straws. Before this, drinkers used natural rye grass straws. Stone made his original straw by winding strips of paper around a pencil and gluing it together. He then used paraffin-coated manila paper, so the straws wouldn't become soggy while someone was drinking. In 1906, Stone's company invented a machine to wind the straws.

Magical Marbles

Rat's Rating

You will need
2 rulers, marbles, sticky tape

Inertia is the way a body will stay still, or move, unless acted upon by an external force.

1 Tape the rulers to a flat surface. They need to be parallel and about 1/2 inch (1.5 cm) apart.

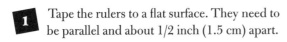

2 Put 2 marbles in the middle of the rulers a few inches (5 cm) apart.

3 Gently tap 1 marble so that it rolls and hits the second one. What happens?

What Happens
The marble that had been rolling stops. And the one that had been still now rolls! The force of the rolling marble transfers to the other one. It stops the first and sets the second one going. Now put two marbles on the stick so they touch and a third marble a short distance away. Gently tap the single marble into the other two. Notice that the rolling marble stops, the middle one stays still and the third one rolls! The momentum went through the second marble into the third! Try other combinations: two marbles into three still marbles, or three into three. You will find that however many marbles you set in motion, the same number will be made to roll when they are hit.

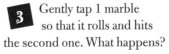

I would have been the wizard of the rat hole as a kid if I'd had these!

ABRACADABRA

MAGIC MARBLES

This one keeps going. This one stops.

Get a Move On

Rat's Rating

You will need
matchbox, stone, small wooden block, eraser, flat sided glass bottle, ice cube or a selection of similar objects, chopping board or smooth piece of wood, metal tray

Do some objects move more easily than others?

1 Put your objects in a line at one end of the chopping board.

2 Slowly lift this end of the board until the objects begin to move. What objects move first?

3 Repeat the experiment but put your objects on a metal tray. Do the objects move more easily?

WOH! Who greased the slide..?

What Happens
Some of your objects will move more easily than others. Feel the ones that move easily. They will feel smooth. Anything rough will not move as easily.

Busy Body

It's Snot Fair!

Rat's Rating

Feel left out when your friends are fussed over because they have colds and you don't? Try making your own mucus! It looks just as revolting as the real stuff, but you don't have to get sick.

You will need
corn syrup/golden syrup, unflavored gelatin, measuring cup, water, microwave oven or stove, green food coloring (optional but it makes the mix look so disgusting), fork

What to do in this anatomy experiment

1 Ask an adult to help you heat 1/2 cup of water until it boils.

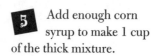

2 Take the pan off the heat. Add a tiny drop of food coloring to the water.

3 Sprinkle in 3 envelopes of unflavored gelatin.

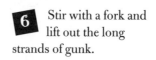

4 Let it soften a few minutes and stir with a fork.

5 Add enough corn syrup to make 1 cup of the thick mixture.

6 Stir with a fork and lift out the long strands of gunk.

7 As it cools, you'll need to add more water, spoonful by spoonful.

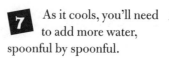

What Happens
You have made fake or artificial mucus.

Why
- Mucus is mainly made out of sugars and protein. That is what you used to make your fake mucus, only you use different proteins and different sugars.
- Those long, fine strings inside your fake mucus are proteins. They are why real mucus can stretch out quite long.
- The protein helps make it sticky, too. The protein in your fake mucus is gelatin.

You wouldn't want to see what's in this hankerchief... IT'S THE REAL THING!

Fun Facts
Put a pinch of fine dust onto your fake mucus. Now stir it up. Look closely into the goo from the side. The fine dust is trapped. That is the why you have mucus in your nose. You use it to trap all the dust, pollen and junk that is floating in the air. With mucus, most of the dirt is trapped and then blown out.

"Eye" Can See Better Than You

29

Rat's Rating

How do animals see the world? Here's your chance to find out. It is a real eye-opener!

You will need
shiny card (or stick a piece of foil to cardstock), cardboard egg carton, scissors, skewer

Will you look at that! If I look like...THIS... I can see like a RAT!

What to do in this zoology experiment

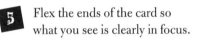

1 Cut a piece of shiny card 12 in. (30 cm) long and 3–1/2 in. (9 cm) wide.

2 Cut an arch about halfway on the card to fit your nose.

3 Put the card to your face. Your nose must fit in the arch, and the card must touch your forehead.

4 Bend the sides of the card slightly away from your head.

5 Flex the ends of the card so what you see is clearly in focus.

6 What is different about the way you now see things?

What Happens
You can see from either side of your head at the same time!

What to do

1 Cut two egg holders from the carton.

2 Using a skewer, make a hole in the bottom of each holder about 1/2 in. (0.5 cm) across. Make sure the holes are a little off center.

HOLE SLIGHTLY TO ONE SIDE

3 Put an egg holder over each of your eyes so the holes point in opposite directions.

Hey! That's wild!

I feel like some sort of BUG!

What Happens
You can see in two different directions!

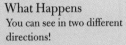

Fun Facts
A television screen shows 24 pictures each second. Because a fly sees 200 images each second, a fly watching television sees it as still pictures with darkness in-between. For a fly's eye view, try to flicker your eyelids very fast.

Why
• The position of an animal's eyes changed over time to suit its needs.
• Our eyes are placed up front. This gives us binocular vision and depth perception. This was vital for an animal that once swung through the trees.
• Animals like horses and rabbits have eyes high and to the sides of their head. This lets them see nearly 360 degrees, as well as far above their head. They have a small blind spot directly in front of their face, but forward placed nostrils and big ears make up for that.
• Chameleons see in different directions at the same time. This way they can watch for danger out of one eye and search for food with the other.

Experiment 30

I am the Walrus

Under their skin, walruses have a layer of fat. Seals and whales have blubber, too. But is that enough to keep them warm when the temperature is below zero? Try this and see!

You will need

two cups, cold water, ice cubes, white fat/lard/shortening (the white stuff an adult uses for baking), paper towels

How's the water?

GREAT!! Just above FREEZING!

What to do in this anatomy experiment

1 Fill two cups with cold water and ice cubes.

2 Stick one of your fingers in each of the cups. How long can you keep your fingers in there before they get too cold? Now think how a walrus would feel diving into the freezing ocean!

3 Make a ball from a piece of the fat. Put one finger in the middle of it. Make sure the finger is completely covered by the fat.

4 Put the fat-covered finger in one of the cups of ice water. Put your other finger in the second cup. Which finger do you want to take out of the cold water first?

Fun Facts

Cold water, less than 70 degrees F (21 degrees C), can lower your body temperature. If your body temperature goes too low when you swim, you may pass out and drown. Your body can cool down 25 times faster in cold water than in air. Long-distance swimmers coat their bodies in fats. A diver's wetsuit gives the same thermal protection as blubber.

What Happens

The fat protects your skin. It stops it from feeling the cold.

I CAN'T STAND THE COLD ANY LONGER!

Why

• Like whales and seals, walruses insulate their bodies with a thick layer of fat called blubber.

• A walrus can change the flow of its blood to adjust its body temperature.

• If a walrus gets too hot, its blood rushes to the blubber and skin. It is cooled by the air or water.

• When a walrus is cold, it can reduce the blood flow to its skin and blubber to save heat.

You just look adorable in all that fat! Are you going my way?

Experiment

31

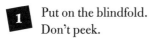

Rat's Rating

Want to find out more?

You will need
a friend, blindfold, item of clothing from
each member of your family

What to do in this biology experiment

1 Put on the blindfold.
Don't peek.

Boy! It's black in here!

2 Ask your friend to get
an item of clothing that
someone has just taken off.
Hopefully, not smelly socks!
Have something from each
member of your family.

3 Get your friend
to hold the
clothing under your
nose. But don't touch it.

Remember the time when the mouse crawled under the refrigerator and died? Well this smells like that!

4 Concentrate and tell
whose clothing it is
just by the smell.

What Happens
You should be able to tell which item of clothing
belongs to each family member.

Why
• The smell comes from the pheromones our
body makes.
• We all have own special smell. The smell is ours
alone and different from anyone else.
• We get used to these smells and don't notice them.
• Our smells even change the fragrance of perfume
or cologne. That's why these are a little different
on every person. It's also the reason different
houses smell differently.

Fun Facts
Be careful not to squash a yellowjacket wasp near
its nest. A dying yellowjacket gives out an alarm
pheromone. This calls other wasps to come and
help. Within 15 seconds, all yellowjackets within a
15 foot (4.5 metre) area will attack you for
squashing their friend!

IT WAS AN ACCIDENT!! I DIDN'T MEAN TO SQUASH YOUR FRIEND!

He had dark hair... medium build... with big boots... and he went that-a-way!

Does This Make Sense?

Blind Test

Rat's Rating

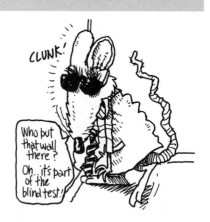

If you were blind, how quickly would you learn to feel your way around? Would it be easier to do some things more than others? Here are some tests to help you find out.

You will need
sheet of paper, sheet of lined paper, pencil

What to do in this biology experiment

1 Place a sheet of paper on a table. Make a circle about 1/2 inch (1.5 cm) around on the paper.

2 Lift your pencil high above your head. Shut your eyes. Lower your arm and make a dot on the paper as close as you can to the center of the circle. How close did you get to the center of the circle? Try again. How many times does it take before you get your dot inside the circle? Now try with your eyes open.

3 On a sheet of lined paper, sign your name.

4 Place your pencil after the signature on the same line. Shut your eyes, and sign your name again. Try writing other words. Can you tell the difference between what you wrote with your eyes closed and what you wrote with your eyes open?

What Happens
You'll make your dot outside the circle at first. It takes several tries before getting inside the circle. With writing your signature there is very little, if any, difference.

Why
• Most people find that looking at the circle between tests makes them do better.
• Your eyesight is very important for real accuracy.
• However, sight is not necessary for copying written words. You are used to the 'feel' of writing from the nerves in your hands and fingers.

Fun Facts
A blind chameleon still changes colors. This is because chameleons don't change colors to match their background. Instead, their color changes are responses to light intensity, temperature, or how they are feeling.

Rat's Rating

Can you always tell the temperature of things you touch?
Perhaps not!

Ever seen sizzled rats paws? Stick around! Mine are nearly done!

You will need

thermometer, lots of different objects that you can touch easily such as: Styrofoam, metal tray, teflon cake pan, plastic tray, tile, brick, piece of cardboard, glass, leather

What to do in this biology experiment

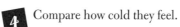

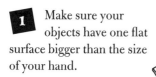

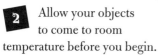

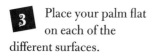

1 Make sure your objects have one flat surface bigger than the size of your hand.

2 Allow your objects to come to room temperature before you begin.

3 Place your palm flat on each of the different surfaces.

4 Compare how cold they feel.

5 Arrange the materials in order from cold to warm.

6 Place the thermometer on each surface. What do you notice?

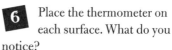

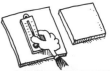

What Happens

All the materials are at the same temperature! Your hand isn't always a good thermometer. When you touch a variety of objects, some will seem warmer or colder than others, even when they are at the same temperature.

Fun Facts

Your skin keeps a constant body temperature of 98.6 degrees Fahrenheit (37 degrees Celsius). When you feel neither hot or cold, you're not aware of the temperature. Keeping you at the right temperature depends on your skin being able to sense a temperature change. That's why you can swim in cold water, yet have a hot bath.

Why

- The nerve endings in your skin are sensitive to temperature.
- They can tell the difference between your inside body temperature and your outside skin temperature.
- When your skin cools, these nerves tell you that the object you're touching is cold.
- An object that feels cold must be colder than your hand. It must carry your body heat away so that your skin cools down.
- Styrofoam and metal are two materials that work well for this experiment. They both start at room temperature and are both colder than your hand.
- They don't feel equally cold because they carry heat away from your hand at different rates.
- Styrofoam is an insulator. This means it is a very poor conductor of heat. When your hand touches the Styrofoam, heat flows from your hand to the Styrofoam and warms its surface. Because this heat is not conducted away quickly, the surface of the Styrofoam becomes as warm as your hand. This means little or no extra heat leaves your hand. There is no difference in temperature between the inside of your body and the outside of your skin. Your nerves sense no difference in temperature. The Styrofoam feels warm.
- Metal carries heat away quickly. Metal is a good conductor of heat. Heat flows from your hand into the metal. It is then conducted quickly away into the bulk of the metal.
- This leaves the metal surface and your skin surface cool. That is why metal feels cool.

Bright Spark: Do You Know What's Watt?

Rat's Rating

Why does the air often crackle when you comb your hair or take off clothes? You'll be 'ecstatic' when you find out.

Who would have thought taking your clothes off in the dark would create an electrical storm!

You will need

a time of year when the air is very dry—winter is a good time (this will not work when the air is humid), scissors, Styrofoam tray from your supermarket (ask at the meat or bakery counter for a clean tray), masking tape, aluminum pie tin

What to do in this electricity experiment

1 Cut a piece from one corner of the Styrofoam tray. You'll have a long bent piece that looks a bit like a hockey stick.

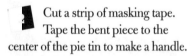

2 Cut a strip of masking tape. Tape the bent piece to the center of the pie tin to make a handle.

3 Rub the bottom of the Styrofoam tray on your hair. Rub it all over, very fast.

4 Put the tray upside down on a table. Use the handle to pick up the pie tin. Hold it about 12 inches (30 cm) over the Styrofoam tray and drop it.

5 Very slowly, touch the tip of your finger to the pie tin. What happens? Don't touch the Styrofoam tray. If you do, nothing will happen!

What Happens

You make a bright spark! Use the handle to pick up the pie tin again. Touch the tin with the tip of your finger. You get another great spark. Drop the pie tin onto the Styrofoam tray again. Touch the pie tin. Another spark! Use the handle to pick up the pie tin. More sparks. If the pie tin stops giving you a spark, just rub the Styrofoam tray on your head again, and start over. Try this experiment in the dark. Can you see the tiny lightning bolts you make? What color are they?

Why

• When you rub Styrofoam on your hair, you pull electrons off your hair and they pile up on the Styrofoam.

• When you put the aluminum pie tin on the Styrofoam, the electrons on the Styrofoam pull on the electrons from the pie tin.

• Some of the electrons in metals are free electrons. This means they move inside the metal.

• Free electrons try to move as far away from the Styrofoam as they can.

• When you touch the pie tin, the free electrons leap to your hand. They spark!

• The pie tin now has fewer electrons. When you lift the pie tin away from the Styrofoam plate, you have a pie tin that attracts all nearby electrons.

Fun Facts

In 1752, Benjamin Franklin flew a kite and string in a thunderstorm. The electricity moved down the string. It made a small spark on the metal key near his hand. This showed that lightning was just a big spark of static electricity. He also invented the lightning rod to protect people, buildings, and ships from lightning. But don't try this at home!

10 seconds after the now famous lightning bolt hit Benjamin's kite... ...a larger and more powerful bolt closed down his experiment...but drove him to invent the lightning rod

COOL INVENTIONS

COOL INVENTIONS

We live in a world full of wonder. Most of the time we take the things around us for granted, but every now and again, our curiosity leads us to ask questions about their origins.

Human beings are unlike any other creature on the planet because of our ability to think, invent, and progress beyond our imagination. Where would we be now if someone had not thought of the idea of the wheel, the computer, or the Ninja Turtle?

This section covers hundreds of inventions from the earliest in history to the wonders of modern science. Also included are some magnificent feats of the imagination and some of the latest buzzwords that have entered our language over the past few years.

There is something in here for everyone, and, who knows, this section may inspire you to be the next great inventor of the twenty-first century!

Contents

1 Tools have been around for three million years! Early people used sharpened stones to cut things up or to chop wood.

2 The first ax may have taken another million years to perfect. This was done simply by sharpening a stone to a thin blade.

3 A few thousand years later, an ax with a heavy base and a longer, straighter edge would have been used.

4 Fire has been around forever! It was easy enough to keep a fire going once it started naturally, but it was a while before people realized they could make fire themselves, through friction caused by two sticks being rubbed together.

5 The act of rolling a stick between the palms of one's hands may also have sparked the idea of a drill as well as fire. A spinning stick could easily burrow its way into the ground.

6 Sharp stones were not only used as weapons. They were also adapted to use as designing tools to carve intricate details on other objects.

7 Cro-Magnon people perfected the art of fishing by using small bones, sharpened with tools tied to plant vines. The 'hook' would lodge in the fish's throat, like a modern steel hook.

8 Different types of tools were experimented with and one, with a sharpened tip rather than a side blade, would become the chisel.

9 Longer sharpened tools made from wood were used for cutting down crops. Later, people worked out that if the blade was curved it would be more time-efficient because it could cut down more crops with each swing.

10 We know that the bow and arrow as a combined weapon has been around for over 30 000 years because it is depicted in cave paintings.

11 The crossbow would come much later. It was invented around 2500 years ago. The first was called a gastrophetes, so named because it was held against the stomach when fired!

12 Ancient cave paintings have provided endless theories as to what they depict, and also what they were painted with. It has been suggested that the first paintbrush was merely a stick that had been chewed at the end until the fibres feathered out into a brush.

13 Early people were resourceful and used much of their surroundings to make useful tools. Plants often proved invaluable; for example, by binding lengths of various vines, the first type of rope was made.

14 People lived in caves for thousands of years but eventually they began to build shelters out of anything they could find, particularly rock, bones, and mud.

15 Just over 7000 years ago people made bricks out of hardened mud with bundled straw inside to strengthen them. It would be another 2000 years before bricks were being baked in a kiln.

16 Around 20 000 years ago, people threw sticks at animals in order to kill them. Eventually, it was realized that certain shapes flew faster and possibly returned to the thrower. This was the first boomerang.

17 The sling is also a very early weapon. It was a simple strap of leather folded double with a stone to hurl held in the fold. Then with a forceful swing, the item was projected through the air.

18 The sling was a useful tool but had its limitations. However, it wasn't until around 400 BC that the catapult was invented. It had far more power and threw much heavier objects—even though they didn't always hit their desired target.

19 The idea of rotation helped with the development of other tools, including the lathe, which cut in a circular pattern when an object was rotated against the blade.

20 Writing wasn't far off; just another 300 years later the Sumerians were marking symbols down in clay in order to keep track of their businesses. Historians have named this early form of writing *cuneiform*.

21 Candles were first used around 5000 years ago and they haven't changed much since. The wick was dipped repeatedly in melted beeswax until it built up to a thick coating.

22 The calendar has had its fair share of alterations. Five thousand years ago the Babylonians had a calendar based on the movement of the sun and moon. However, the Egyptians were aware of how inaccurate this could be, so relied only on the sun.

23 It was the Babylonians who devised the sixty seconds in a minute and sixty minutes in an hour calculation that we use to this day.

24 It wasn't until 45 BC that Julius Caesar decided to create a new calendar based on a 365-day year. He even called it the Julian calendar, after himself!

25 Pope Gregory XIII invented the Gregorian calendar in 1582. This new calendar was based on Julius Caesar's but he omitted a few days so the seasons always fell into place. We still use this perfected form today.

26 The ancient Egyptians were not the sort of people to let things get in the way of progress. When the city of Memphis was under threat of flooding from the rising Nile, they built what is likely to have been the very first dam.

27 Ancient Egyptians were also the inventors of the forerunner of paper: papyrus. They flattened reeds until they became bound together. Then they polished the sheets with stones to make them even flatter and smoother for writing on.

28 The ink used by ancient Egyptians to write on papyrus was a combination of glue and soot. It was initially dry, so it had to be moistened before use.

After only ten minutes into his job as royal scribe, Akhenaten realized that dry papyrus ink and a black tongue were not for him... So decided his old day job dragging rocks around the pyramids was not so bad after all.

29 Later on, around 2400 BC, a form of leather that was treated to be paler than most was used to write upon. This was to become known as parchment.

30 The heating of sand with limestone produces glass, and for many years glass was used mainly for ornamental purposes. The ancient Egyptians would eventually work with it. They began to make glass containers 3500 years ago.

31 It wasn't until 1300 AD that glass mirrors were made by the Venetians. Before that, shiny metals such as silver and bronze were the main reflective surfaces used by vain people!

What's this? It looks like water! Go quickly, Hamadi! Go build a dam across the Nile. And make it snappy!

King Cheops appoints his first Minister for Dams when he finds the palace half full of water.

I wish somebody could invent a decent mirror. These shiny metal mirrors make me look... well... all wobbly and fuzzy ...and ugly!

32 It has been suggested that the ancient Egyptians were the first people to invent tongs, most likely as a way to hold their glass creations in the fire as they heated them.

33 As time moved on, people began to develop a sense of hygiene. Eventually, the concept of separate areas for washing began to take shape. Approximately 4000 years ago, people in India built homes with drainage systems to carry waste away from living areas.

34 Running water was a surprisingly late invention, even though there had been bathrooms in India. It was the royalty of Crete at the palace of King Minos who had the first pipe system installed around 1700 BC.

35 Flags were invented by the Chinese around 1500 BC. They were significant to the owner, but were even more so to the enemy of the owner. The flag captured during battle would signify defeat!

Carry the flag for five minutes would you me old chum... just to give my arms a rest.

No way matey! They always shoot the guy who's carrying the flag!

36 Although the Greeks invented metal body armor in 800 BC, the Chinese were making their own 300 years earlier out of the skin of the rhinoceros, which is incredibly thick and strong.

37 Chain mail was a way of making armor lighter and easier to move in and was invented by the Greeks in 200 BC.

38 The Greeks discovered the first magnetic rock around 3000 years ago in a place called Magnesia, which gave the mineral its name.

39 Oil has been used for burning and providing a light source for thousands of years. Around 700 BC, the Greeks created lamps with wicks sitting in a pool of oil. The Chinese and Egyptians used similar lamps even earlier.

40 The Egyptians were also the pioneers of the sundial, or certainly a distant relative of one—the shadow clock. The sun would cast a shadow and, depending on where the shadow was on a scale of marked hours, one could tell the time of day.

Amun! Using your new sundial, ...what time do you make it?

Oh... looks like 2 PM to me!

Oh! I'm late! I had a lunch date at the Sphinx at 1pm

41 The first waterwheel was used by the Greeks in a corn mill just over 2000 years ago. This was so successful that it wasn't long before the Romans made larger models. Waterwheels are still in use today.

Oh!

Taking his newly invented abacus for a test run multiplying 584 sheep by 620 dates, divided by 12 clay jars of olives... Uruk discovers a major mechanical problem with the abacus and has to shut down the calculation.

42 The abacus may have been invented around 2400 BC by the Babylonians but we do know it was also used by the Chinese and the Romans.

43 The first chairs of a design we are familiar with today may well be nearly 5000 years old. Carved seats and thrones have been found in the tombs of ancient Egyptian kings.

I'm the Pharaoh of all Egypt... They give me gold, jewels, precious stones, chariots, slaves and expensive carved furniture. You'd think someone could find me a soft cushion to sit on!

44 Carpets were also created by the ancient Egyptians, who wove their own.

45 Linoleum, however, was a much later invention. In 1861, Frederick Walton, a British rubber manufacturer, wanted to make a smooth, washable floor surface. He worked to create a substance made from linseed oils and other materials, and invented linoleum (or lino). It is still used today.

46 Although James King first invented a washing machine with a drum in 1851, Alva J. Fisher invented the first electric machine in 1908.

Oohh! Well if nothing else... it got the stains out!

James King's wife tries out her husband's new invention... The washing machine.

47 In 1903 Herbert Booth became the brains behind the vacuum cleaner, although it was the Hoover that became the most famous design.

48 Percy Spencer invented the microwave oven in 1946. He was an engineer for the Raytheon Company in the USA, and while he was experimenting with radar, he found some candy had melted in his pockets. This gave him the idea for the microwave oven.

While standing just that bit too close to the radar he was working on with a pocket full of candy... Engineer Percy Spencer accidentally invents the microwave oven ...and even more importantly... IRRADIATED TOFFEE!

49 Sir John Harrington built the first toilet for his godmother, Queen Elizabeth of England, in 1596. He was ridiculed for the idea and never made any more. Although many inventors copied the style, it wasn't until 1885 that Thomas Twyford built the classic china bowl rather than the original wooden sort.

50 The sewing machine had many prototypes from many different inventors around the world. The first successful one was the brainchild of a Frenchman, Barthelemy Thimonier, in 1830. Sadly, a group of angry tailors ransacked his factory for fear of unemployment.

51 In 1851, Dr John Gorrie came up with the idea of a refrigerator, inspired by his plan to keep fevered patients cool through pressured gas. Nearly a decade later, Ferdinand Carre would develop the idea further to make the refrigerators we are accustomed to today.

52 There have been many variations on the lock over the past 4000 years. Many inventors have had variable success with their designs but it is the name Linus Yale Jr that goes down in history, after he invented the cylinder pin-tumble lock in 1861.

53 Levi Hutchins of New Hampshire invented the first mechanical alarm clock in 1787. The only problem was the alarm would only go off at four o'clock!

54 Soap was not always used for washing. For many years a soap-like mixture of fat and ash was used for medicinal purposes, but in the second century the Romans made a similar compound to clean items and themselves.

55 The thermostats that are in use today have a history that dates back to approximately 1600, when a Dutchman named Cornelius Drebbel combined the thermometer with a damper in a furnace.

56 Light bulbs wouldn't exist in their current form if it were not for the discovery of tungsten. Tungsten is the material within the bulb that heats up and glows brightly. Two brothers from Spain, Fausto and Juan D'Elhuyar, were the first to discover this ingenious way of producing light with tungsten in 1783.

57 Thomas Edison and Joseph Swan both independently came up with the idea of using carbon within a light bulb to create light in the mid-1800s. By the end of the nineteenth century, light bulbs were being used in most places around the world.

Life at midnight before the light bulb was invented.

Life at midnight after the lightbulb was invented.

58 Cement used for building is also known as Portland cement and was invented by Joseph Aspdin in 1824. He was a British builder, and he mixed limestone and clay to form a stronger substance.

59 The can-opener was invented by Robert Yeates in 1855. It was a simple sharp blade that was jammed into the top of the can and moved around the rim. Before that, cans were opened using a hammer and chisel.

60 The ring-pull (initially on drink cans, but eventually stronger versions on food tins) was invented by Ermal Fraze in 1966.

61 Fiberglass is often used for insulation in modern homes. It was invented by Russell Games Slayter in 1938 and is made from extremely fine glass fibers.

62 The skyscraper is a tall building with a steel frame, and the first one was merely ten stories high. It was built in Chicago in the USA in 1885 and was designed by William Jenney.

63 The cat flap is one of Isaac Newton's lesser-known inventions, but all the same, he devised the mini door for the cat back in the seventeenth century!

64 Although people were able to communicate through speech and, for a long time, through the aid of pictures, it wasn't until around 3000 years ago that the first written languages appeared. The Greeks adapted a system from the Palestinians using patterns of consonants and vowels. This was a distant relative of the alphabet we know today.

65 Hieroglyphics are a form of writing developed by the ancient Egyptians (although not exclusively). Pictures were used to represent words, letters, and concepts. A quail chick, an owl, a reed, and a vulture are just a few of the symbols to represent letters.

66 Sign language was not the invention of one person. It came into existence through necessity, as people who were deaf had to find a way to communicate. Just as there are different spoken languages, there are also different sign languages.

67 The very first postage stamp was made in Great Britain in 1840. It was called the Penny Black and it had a picture of Queen Victoria's head on it. It was invented by Rowland Hill and it was adhesive, enabling it to be stuck to an envelope. Hill was knighted for his work.

68 Chinese whispers is a game where players pass on a sentence by whispering it to another player. It is passed on again, until after a number of repetitions the information is shared, usually much altered. A story about its origins tells how an officer sent the message 'Send reinforcements, we're going to advance' along a relay of soldiers, only for it to reach the intended recipient as 'Send three and four pence, we're going to a dance'!

69 Pencils were an idea of Conrad Gesner from Germany, who took the soft material of carbon and encased it in wood in 1565.

70 Around 2500 years ago, ancient Greeks used pens that were made of wood. The wood was sharpened to a point and had a groove leading down to the tip through which ink could flow.

71 One of the first postal services was in 1653, in France. A maker of envelopes called De Valayer offered to deliver any mail placed into the mail boxes he provided, but only on the condition that his envelopes were used.

72 The QWERTY keyboard which is now standard was designed and patented by Christopher Sholes in 1868. It made typing easier by not placing too many common pairs of letters together and enabled two-hand typing to flow without the constant need to unblock the typewriter's lettered arms. It is interesting to note that the word 'typewriter' can be typed out easily across the top row of letters!

73 Morse code was the invention of Samuel Morse in 1832. Morse came up with the idea of an electromagnetic telegraph system while talking to a colleague, and then proceeded to jot down the dot-dash system into his notebook. However, he didn't apply for the patent until 1837.

74 The telephone was invented by Alexander Graham Bell, who was in competition with rival inventor, Elisha Gray. On 10 March in 1876, Bell succeeded with his creation and by 1877 he had begun his own telephone company.

75 David Hughes invented the printing telegraph in 1855. The first machines using Morse code seemed a little complicated so he made a machine that could send written messages and have them printed out at the other end.

76 Radio has a complex history but the names most people remember as having a part in its invention are Guglielmo Marconi and Nikola Tesla, who discovered how to transmit data over a wireless connection using the electromagnetic wave spectrum.

77 In 1892, the combined efforts of Oliver Heaviside and physicist Michael Pupin helped to improve long distance cabling for telephone wires through the addition of recurring coils along the line.

78 Today, just about everyone who is old enough owns a mobile or cellular phone, and it is hard to think of life without one. It all started back in 1979 in the Bell Telephone Laboratories in the USA. It took many years for mobile phones to reduce in size and become readily available to the public.

The early MOBILE PHONE

79 The modem is for sending and receiving data over telephone lines and decoding digital information. Its name is derived from the term modulator/demodulator. Modems were first sold commercially by AT&T in 1962.

80 The first telegraph cable to stretch across the Atlantic was laid in 1858 by a group of scientists. Although the first line failed after a few weeks, it paved the way for future successful attempts.

81 The first microphone was invented by Emile Berliner in 1877 but the first practical design was invented by Alexander Graham Bell. Berliner would eventually work for the Bell Company until 1883.

82 Hearing aids were once large funnels held up to a deaf person's ear and were known as 'ear-trumpets'. The electronic hearing aid was invented by various people. Depending on the size of the battery, the devices are practically invisible when worn in the ear.

83 The first harps were used around 5000 years ago and have been linked to Egypt and Samaria. These early instruments were curved sticks with strings strung from end to end with various tensions.

84 The lyre was similar to the harp. This ancient instrument also had strings but they were stretched over the frame of a bowl or a box.

85 Another very early instrument was the bell, which 4000 years ago would be hung from a frame and then be struck by small hammers during religious events.

86 An early form of trumpet is actually the Australian didgeridoo. Rams' horns were also used in a similar way in the Middle East. It was the ancient Egyptians, however, who made the first metal trumpet, out of silver.

87 Bartolomeo Cristofori designed the piano in 1698, although the final perfected model was not finished until 1720. It was based on a harpsichord design but was more complex, with a much more resonant sound.

88 The flute is just over 2000 years old, although there were simpler forms of pipes for thousands of years. The instrument we are familiar with today has its origins in China. It is a hollow pipe with finger holes, and a reed which vibrates when blown into.

89 The very first drum was played around 8000 years ago. It was a simple instrument made from the hide of an animal stretched over a hollow object and strapped tightly down.

2000 years ago in China while Wong was building a duck pen, he accidentally picked up a stick of bamboo, drilled holes in it and put it in his mouth and invented the flute... The ducks just ran away.

90 Thomas Edison made the first phonograph to record sound in 1877. The first sound recorded on it was 'Mary had a Little Lamb'.

91 Swiss-born Adolf Rickenbacker moved to the USA when he was a child. He went on to create the very first electric guitar in 1932.

92 The first electronic instrument, however, was the Theremin. Invented in 1920 by Leon Theremin from Russia, it is played by moving the hands around two antennae without actually touching the instrument.

Jurst leesen to thees leetle beauty, comrade. When they heer thees they will dance ol ov the way to Siberia.

Let Us Entertain You

93 The accordion actually has many inventors and various designs. Among its inventors are Bernhard Eschenbach in 1810, Christian Buschmann in 1822, and Pichenot Jeune in 1831.

94 The patent for the saxophone was registered in 1846 by Adolphe Sax from Belgium. He made fourteen different types of saxophone during his lifetime.

Before inventing the SAXOPHONE Adolphe Sax works on some earlier prototypes including the MONSTERPHONE.

95 One of the very first musical instruments was the whistle. It was first invented over ten thousand years ago, possibly when someone blew over a tube-shaped item such as a bone or a piece of bamboo and produced sounds.

96 The first captured motion on film was of a racehorse galloping. In 1877, the horse's owner asked British man Eadweard Muybridge to find a way of telling whether a horse's hooves were ever all off the ground at the same time. A relay of cameras along a track took pictures one after the other, and the sequence of images proved that the hooves were often all off the ground at once. This led to developments in motion picture making.

97 In 1886, Chichester Bell and Charles Tainter improved the first sound recordings. At first, recordings were made on foil wrapped around a cylinder, but this was not very satisfactory and incredibly fragile. The two American inventors recorded onto wax cylinders that were more resilient and lasted for years. Their machine was called the graphophone.

98 The gramophone was invented in 1887 by Emile Berliner and was able to play discs of recorded sound using the same principle as Bell and Tainter's graphophone. The needle was aligned in the groove on the disc, recreating the sounds and projecting them through the horn to amplify them.

99 In 1893, William Dickson took the idea further and managed to take forty pictures a second and lay them out onto a strip of film that could be viewed through a device called a kinetoscope. These 'films' were only twenty seconds long, but did show an animated image.

100 Television was invented by John Logie Baird in the 1920s. By 1930, the BBC in the United Kingdom aired the first televised play, which was called *The Man with a Flower in His Mouth*.

101 Television wouldn't exist at all if it were not for the cathode ray oscilloscope. Ferdinand Braun invented it in 1897 and it works by decoding electrical messages and displaying them on a screen.

102 Video tape recording was invented in 1951 by Charles P. Ginsberg. It was able to retain images and sound on magnetic tape that could be viewed again and again. The first VCR (video cassette recorder) wasn't available to the public until 1971.

Ahhrrgg! I've been stuck in traffic, got home late and missed my favourite soapy "Tomorrow Never Comes"

Now I'll never know if Paula married Brad...whether Cynthia went to New York or if Ramone was really taken by aliens. First thing in the morning I'm going to invent the videotape...So I don't miss another episode.

103 DVDs were not the first form of disk in the revolution that replaced tapes. Laser disks were available much earlier and they were an extension of David Paul Gregg's optical disk, which he invented in 1958. DVDs (digital versatile disks) soon took over as they were a vast improvement in sound and picture quality, and they were much smaller.

104 James T. Russell from Washington in the United States developed the concept of the compact disk in the latter half of the 1960s because he was frustrated with the poor sound quality of vinyl disks and tapes.

105 It wasn't until the 1980s that the two companies, Philips and Sony, mass produced the CD format. The first CD players arrived in 1982.

106 The first public radio broadcasts came in 1920, in Britain. This service was started by Guglielmo Marconi. Later the same year a similar service began in the USA.

107 Atari was the leading computer game manufacturer in the late 70s and early 80s. The founders were Nolan Bushnell and Ted Dabney, who initially made game consoles for amusement arcades. In the mid 1970s, they developed the first home video game, called 'Pong'.

108 The computer mouse has been around since 1963 when Douglas Engelbart invented it, although back then it was a much bulkier tool.

109 Apple Computer hired Tony Fadell when he approached them with the concept of the iPod®, one of the first successful portable music players that can carry much more music than a cassette tape or CD.

110 Disco was a music and dance craze beginning in the early 1970s, and has been heavily inspired by soul music and funk.

111 In 1979, Sony designed a portable music system that was the height of fashion during the 80s. It was named the Walkman® and played cassette tapes. However, these are now pretty much obsolete with the advent of CDs and iPods®.

112 Karaoke has long been part of Japanese social tradition, but the first karaoke machine was the brainwave of Daisuke Inoue in the 1970s. He pre-recorded songs for people to sing along to at parties when a 100-yen coin was inserted.

113 The Fraunhofer Institute in Germany created mp3, a system that compresses music, making it easier to download from the Internet.

114 Although there has been debate over who invented the first cinema, it is widely believed to be the Lumière brothers, Auguste and Louis. Their projector gave its first public performance in 1895.

Louis, did you bring the matches to light the lamp in the projector?

No, Auguste... I thought you were going to buy them from the grocery store on the way here.

Do you think we should sit here in the dark eating our popcorn or should we go climb the Eiffel tower instead, my sweet?

OPENING NIGHT AT THE FIRST CINEMA IN 1895.

115 In 1832, there was a device that enabled people to see pictures in 3D. It was called the stereoscope and allowed each eye to focus on a separate image. The combined result would give a three-dimensional effect. It was created by Charles Wheatstone and improved upon by David Brewster in 1851.

116 Computer-generated effects in movies were developed in the early 1980s and were made possible due to computers designed by James Clark. Originally intending his work for military use, he was surprised when the movie world embraced the technology to create fantastic images on-screen.

They'll never phase out actors like me, darling. I'm simply irreplaceable!

Don't bet on it. I've only just come from seeing a movie that had no actors in it at all! Everything was computer generated.

117 Film soundtracks in the early days of silent movies were either played live or recorded on gramophone discs. In 1926, Lee de Forest added a thin strip of soundtrack down the side of the film so words and picture were in sync.

118 The modern horror 'slasher' movie was a relatively new concept when Alfred Hitchcock introduced the world to *Psycho*, the first movie of its kind.

119 The first full-length CGI (computer generated imagery) movie was released in 1995. *Toy Story* was made by Disney and Pixar, and many other films followed.

120 Virtual reality is a concept that has been around in science fiction for years. In 1987, a data glove was invented by a musician in the USA called Tom Zimmerman. He wanted to reproduce into a computer the hand gestures associated with playing an instrument. The glove is able to copy the movements of the hand and recon-struct it in a virtual reality program.

121 The very first television commercial aired in the USA on 1 July 1941 and advertised Bulova clocks and watches!

Hey! What's the big idea? Here I am just relaxing watching the test pattern when someone comes on trying to sell me clocks of all things! I don't need a clock! I've had enough. What time is it? I'm going to bed.

122 The first full-length animated feature film was also from Disney. It was *Snow White and the Seven Dwarfs* in 1937.

123 Big Brother was originally a frightening concept thought up by George Orwell for his novel *1984* in which the human race was constantly under surveillance. The TV reality show was an idea inspired by Orwell's vision and came from the mind of John DeMol who took his game show idea to a TV company in the Netherlands. It has since become a worldwide phenomenon.

124 Comic books have their origins in newspaper comic strips. Eventually, comic strips became so popular that they were extended into the comic book format and finally into full graphic novels.

125 Puppets as an art form have been around since the ancient Greeks used to perform with shadow puppets. Much later, the stringed variety would come into popular culture and be known as marionettes.

126 Rollercoasters were developed by John Miller and his first partner, Norman Bartlett. Built in 1926, the first rollercoaster was known as the 'Flying Turns' ride. Later, Miller would go on to devise further rollercoaster rides with his new partner, Harry Baker.

127 Bumper cars have been a part of the fun fair for most of the twentieth century. One of the first companies to make them was the Dodgem Corporation, which gave them their nickname of 'Dodgem cars'. The company was founded by a group of previously battling inventors all out to claim the invention as their own.

128 Carousels in some form or another have been around since 500 AD, originally in the Byzantine Empire. Early carousels were very primitive and it wasn't until the late nineteenth century that steam-powered versions appeared in Europe. The early 1900s saw a golden age of the carousel in America where more and more extravagant designs were created.

129 To celebrate the 400th anniversary of Columbus' discovery of the US, the World's Fair was held in 1893 in Chicago. A bridge-building engineer named George Ferris was asked to design and build an attraction, and he came up with what is now known as the Ferris wheel.

130 Trampolines are said to have originated from an idea used by the Inuit, who played with stretched walrus skin to toss each other into the air. However, in 1936 a circus performer named George Nissen built an apparatus in his garage which was the prototype of the modern trampoline.

131 The house of mirrors is often found at carnivals and theme parks. It usually consists of a maze-like path through a room of mirrors. The mirrors can be curved into different shapes, producing distorted reflections. The inspiration for the house of mirrors is thought to be the spectacular hall of mirrors in Palace of Versailles in France, which was completed in 1684.

132 The horseshoe was a late invention considering the centuries of riding horses that had gone before. Around 150 BC, leather coverings were strapped to horses' hooves to protect them and help horses walk further more comfortably. Metal shoes with nails were not invented for another 600 years.

You don't have any shoes in pink leather, do you? I think the white clashes with my hide.

And something comfortable too! I've got a lot of walking to do.

133 Skateboards were invented by surfers, who attached roller skates to plywood boards back in the 1950s. Over the years, the boards were refined. The wheels became smaller, and the axles became stronger.

134 The elevator or lift has been around in some form for centuries. It works by using a pulley system to raise items up and lower them again. It wasn't until 1880 that a German inventor called Werner von Siemens invented the first modern lift.

135 The Zeppelin company made its first airship in 1900 after spending ten years designing it. Originally airships were filled with hydrogen but this was found to be too dangerous, as hydrogen becomes flammable when combined with air. Helium proved to be a suitable replacement.

136 Perhaps one of the most graceful modes of transport is the hot air balloon. The French Montgolfier brothers designed and built their balloon in 1783, and paved the way towards later airships and blimps.

137 Who would have thought that the common escalator often found in shopping malls was originally an amusement ride? The very first idea came from Charles Wheeler in 1892 but it wasn't until 1897 that Jesse W. Reno created one for the Coney Island amusement park in New York.

138 In 1919, George Hansburg created a device called the pogo stick, which was a toy for bouncing up and down on. It had a metal frame with a spring inside it, a bar for the feet to stand on, and a handle at the top. More recently, the pogo stick has been developed into the Flybar®.

139 In 1863 American inventor James Plimpton attached four wheels to each shoe to create the forerunner of the modern-day roller skates.

140 Although horse-drawn wagons ran along wooden railroads in Germany as far back as 1550, it wasn't until 1804 that a man called Richard Trevithick built the first steam locomotive.

Giddee up Ginger! Technology is catching up with us, old girl!

141 Two men in different times and places invented the electric motor. English engineer, William Sturgeon, invented the commutator in 1832. An American, Thomas Davenport, also invented one in 1834. This device alternates the current to keep a motor running.

142 The automobile or motor car has a debatable history. There were simultaneous projects around the world working on the concept, and there was a big court case at the beginning of the twentieth century between George Selden, who had patented a multi-cylinder vehicle but never actually completed a finished model, and Henry Ford, who did build his model. Selden lost his patent when the judge ordered a model of his design to be built and it failed to operate!

143 Humankind dreamed of being able to fly for thousands of years. In 1903, Wilbur and Orville Wright, two brothers from Ohio, in the USA, made the first successful manned flight. It only lasted twelve seconds but the following year, after alterations and improvements were made, they succeeded in a five-minute flight.

144 Parachutes were first drawn by none other than Leonardo Da Vinci. A man from Croatia named Faust Vrancic made a kind of parachute based on the design and tested it out in 1617, in Venice.

145 In 1783, Louis Lenormand from France improved on the parachute design and tested it by jumping off the roof of the Montpellier observatory safely.

FAUST VRANCIC CHOOSES VENICE TO TEST HIS PARACHUTE IN 1617 AS HE DIDN'T HAVE A LOT OF CONFIDENCE IN HIS INVENTION AND CRASH LANDING INTO WATER FROM A THREE-STORY BUILDING SEEMED MORE APPEALING THAN LANDING ON SOLID GROUND.

146 The first military submarine was designed by an American called David Bushnell in 1776. It was called 'The Turtle'. The submarine was just big enough to hold one man and it submerged by taking water into the hull. It could return to the surface by pumping out the water with a hand pump.

147 Boats have been made in many different ways: a hollowed out tree, wood panels bound together with animal skins, or, as the ancient Egyptians did over 8000 years ago, fashioned from reeds tied tightly together.

148 The catamaran was actually the invention of a fishing community in India. The two-hulled boat is held together by a simple frame. The name comes from the Indian word 'kattumaram' which simply means 'logs bound together'.

149 Canals are man-made rivers connecting larger water sources. They have been used to transport boats (barges and riverboats) for many years. The earliest canals date back 6000 years to ancient Mesopotamia.

150 The first motorbike was the Gottlieb Daimler. It was invented in 1885 but was greatly inspired by the various gasoline-fueled automobiles and internal combustion engines designed by Karl Benz, Nicolaus Otto, and Henry Ford.

151 The Jet Ski® (a registered trademarked name) was designed by Clayton Jacobsen II of Arizona in 1973, who was initially a motocross enthusiast. This is why there are similarities between the Jet Ski and a motorbike!

152 In 1956, Christopher Cockerell invented the first hovercraft, a vehicle that could travel over land and water on a fan-powered cushion of air. However, the idea was not new. In 1716, a Swedish designer named Emanuel Swedenborg came up with the concept but a vehicle was never built.

153 The street car/tram/cable car was invented by Andrew Hallidie who, in 1873, designed a system to pull vehicles up the steep hills in San Francisco in the USA by running wire ropes along channels in the roads. These became the cable cars which are still in use today. There are variations of this design across the world, some using overhead electric cables.

Boy! Am I glad we don't have to walk up these steep hills in San Francisco!

Say, friend! Weren't we traveling uphill a minute ago?

154 The very first fire engine was horsedrawn and its water was pumped out through a tube using steam power. It was invented by John Braithwaite in 1829 and went through many improvements over the years.

155 Although the Chinese had a flying propeller toy over 2000 years ago and Leonardo Da Vinci drew sketches of a concept in 1490, Paul Cornu invented the modern helicopter in 1907. Unfortunately, his designs were not altogether successful.

Paul, my good friend. Thankyou for taking me on your first flight. But I'm finding it a little hard to see the scenery.

Of course! How silly of me! We need a rear tail rotor to stop us from spinning!

THE FIRST HELICOPTER HAD JUST A FEW PROBLEMS

156 John Hetrick patented a design for airbags as far back as 1952. Allen Breed invented a similar design in 1967. Initially just for the driver, they are now fitted into the passenger side of cars. In the event of a collision, the bags will immediately inflate and protect the driver or passenger from hitting their head or chest on anything hard.

157 Frederick Lanchester invented the disk brake in 1902, and air brakes, used on trains, were the brainchild of George Westinghouse in 1872.

158 A Royal National Lifeboat Association inspector in the UK named Captain Ward took the basic idea of cork flotation blocks as used by Norwegian seamen and made vests in 1854 for the lifeboat crews. These were for weather protection as well as an aid to buoyancy in the sea.

159 In 1923, the 'stop' and 'go' signs in the USA came into use. This system was designed by Garrett Morgan.

Woah, boy! That was a close call! That guy wasn't going to stop at that sign.

A SCENE AT AN INTERSECTION IN WEST VIRGINIA IN 1923.

Well, Fraird... That looked like wern of those noo fandangled STOP airnd GO sarns. But heck! I cairnt read wern from the other anyway!

160 The very first subway/metro/underground was the Cobble Hill Tunnel in Brooklyn, New York, in 1850. London's first underground railway opened in 1863.

161 SCUBA is an acronym for self-contained underwater breathing apparatus and was coined by the US Navy in 1939. Throughout history, many inventors have attempted to create apparatus for underwater breathing. Some, including Sieur Freminet in France and Henry Fleuss from England, died in the process!

162 The modern version of wheelchairs was invented in 1932 by engineer Harry Jennings because he had a friend named Herbert Everest who was an invalid. Four hundred years ago, an invalid chair was designed for King Phillip II of Spain.

163 Ambulances were used in their earliest horse-drawn form during conflicts such as the American Civil War (1861–1865) and the French Napoleonic Wars (1799–1815).

164 Sir Frank Whittle of Britain and Hans von Ohain of Germany invented the turbo jet engine in the 1930s. However, they never worked together and didn't know of the other's designs.

165 The Concorde began as a collaborative design between the British, French, Americans, and Soviets in an attempt to develop supersonic air transport back in the 1950s. Because the project was so expensive, it took a couple of decades to get it up in the air. The first Concorde commercial flight was not until 1976 and the last one was in 2003, when the planes were retired.

166 The wheel is renowned for being one of our earliest inventions. It enabled people to move large objects, create pulley systems, and, eventually, travel great distances with ease.

167 One of the first wheeled vehicles was the chariot around 3500 BC. It was to continue to be an invaluable means of transport for many centuries.

168 Rickshaws have been in use in Japan since 1868. The passenger sits in a sheltered seat above two large wheels and a man pulls from the front as he runs. The original rickshaw inventor is unknown, but it may have been an American named Jonathan Scobie, whose wife was an invalid. He needed some form of transport for her while they were in Japan.

169 Wheelbarrows were, oddly, a rather late invention. They didn't appear until sometime during the first century. They were used initially by European workmen and miners.

170 The hang-glider was originally an idea from NASA. It was suggested as a way for astronauts to safely return to the Earth's surface. Technician Francis Rogallo set about creating the contraption in 1948. Further developments continued in Australia, where the concept was perfected. Hang-gliding is now a popular sport.

171 Robert Fulton from the USA invented the first successful steam ship in 1807. Many others attempted to do so but they managed only a few voyages before complications arose – like falling to pieces from the tremendous vibrations of their engines.

172 Dice were an early invention from around 4000 years ago. They did not always have dots—some had runes or other symbols. Dice were often used as a way of telling the future.

173 Monopoly® has a confusing history with lawsuits surrounding the claims as to who actually invented it. Some say it was Charles Darrow in 1930 and some say it was Lizzie Magie in 1906. Maybe we will never learn the truth!

174 Two Canadians named Scott Abbott and Chris Haney invented Trivial Pursuit® in 1979, but it was a couple of years before it was released to the general public. During the 1980s it became a worldwide phenomenon.

175 In the 1930s, Alfred Butts devised a game in which players would put together words with letters written on small cardboard squares. Over time, the game was known as 'Lexico', 'It' and 'Criss-cross'. It became Scrabble® in 1948.

176 Bingo originated in Italy in 1530, where it was a form of lotto. Early versions of the game in the USA were called 'Beano' because beans were used to cover up the numbered squares.

DONATELLO HAS A BIG WIN AT THE FIRST BINGO HALL IN ITALY IN 1530.

177 Chess is around 4000 years old and originated in Persia and India. However, it wasn't until the 1840s that a super chess champion named Howard Staunton designed the pieces we play with today.

178 Soccer is one of the earliest versions of the game of football known to man and there are many historical references to the game in China, Greece, and Italy. Today's game, and its rules, date back to nineteenth-century England when it was popular with boys' schools.

179 Basketball was invented by a Canadian teacher called James Naismith in 1891. He took a basket and a regular football into the gymnasium, and attempted to pitch the ball into the goal.

180 The French invented the first form of tennis in the twelfth century, although it was then called 'Paulme' meaning 'palm' because the ball was struck with the palm of the hand.

181 Golf can be traced back to a game played by the Scots in the fifteenth century. Players would use sticks to hit small stones on sand dunes!

182 Rugby is a sport that takes its history from the game of soccer and has two separate forms, Rugby League and Rugby Union. Legend has it that, in 1823, William Webb Ellis, a young player of the game at Rugby School, in England, picked up the ball and ran with it. Rugby is the forerunner of American football.

183 American football was given its own rules in 1879 by a football coach named Walter Camp. Along with baseball, it is now one of the country's biggest sports.

184 Ice skates have been discovered dating back as far as 3000 BC! Made from animal bone with leather straps, they were found in a lake in Switzerland.

185 Baseball was around in the early nineteenth century in America but the modern baseball field and the first rules were invented by Alexander Cartwright in 1845, and have evolved into the modern game.

186 Ice hockey has been around in Europe for centuries but the rules in use today were devised by Canadian J. G. A. Creighton, in 1875.

187 A young man named William Morgan from Massachusetts invented the game of volleyball in 1895. He originally named it 'mintonette'.

188 Paintball has a surprising history, as it was not invented as a sport. Forestry commissioners designed a gun that emitted paint pellets for marking trees in areas difficult to access. The game evolved after some of the people marking the trees started fooling around and firing at each other!

Karl, a forestry worker, can't understand why his work mates keep picking on him with paint balls.

189 Cricket has a very long history, dating as far back as 1300. It is said to have originated in the south of England and was played by farmers. Now cricket is one of the most popular sports in the world.

190 The Olympic Games as a concept has been around for centuries. The first recorded games were in 776 BC in ancient Greece. The modern games began in 1896 and are generally held every four years.

Race you to the other side of the Parthenon, Aesepus! Last one there is a rotten piece of Baklava!

THE FIRST OLYMPIC GAMES IN ANCIENT GREECE.

191 The Commonwealth Games started in 1930, and were then called the British Empire Games. This competition is also held every four years. The competing countries are all part of the British Commonwealth.

So how often do we need to have these confounded Empire Games or Commonwealth Games...or whatever they're called?

Let's make them every four years, High Chancellor. It will take me that long to train up for the hundred-yard dash.

192 Othello® (also known as Reversi®), a simple yet brilliant game of skill, was invented by Goro Hasegawa from Japan in 1971. It has been an addictive game ever since.

193 Sudoku was originally invented by an American, suitably named Howard Games, in 1979 for a New York newspaper. It started a massive craze in Japan when introduced there in 1984. The name 'sudoku' roughly translates to 'single numbers'.

194 Poker has a very complicated history and it is not definite where the origins of the game lie. However, it may be connected to the French game 'Poque' or the English game 'Brag'. Today it is more popular than ever, even being played on television as a spectator sport!

195 The Fitness Corporation invented the Abdominizer® (a stomach workout device) in 1982. However, many people managed to injure themselves while using one, so better models had to be made to overcome these problems.

196 Exercise bikes have changed in style over the years, though nowadays the bikes can be adjusted to varying degrees of speed and pressure.

197 The cross-trainer is designed to exercise different parts of your body at once. There are various designs but all have the same purpose of improving the cardio-vascular system and muscle tone.

198 Treadmills enable people to run without leaving the room. They can control the speed of the conveyor belt and the incline of a hill through the push of a button.

199 Gym balls, also known as Swiss balls or fit balls, are relatively new pieces of gym equipment. When used, the body tries to balance with the ball, exercising the stomach and back muscles to work as they should. Some people substitute their chair at work with a gym ball to aid their posture.

200 Swimming pools have been around since ancient Greek and Roman times. In 1837, six indoor pools were built in London and it was the modern Olympic Games in 1896 that inspired more people to use pools.

201 Sunscreen or suntan lotion was made in 1936 by Eugene Schueller and was an oil to prevent the skin being burned by the harmful rays of the sun. Today, his company is known as L'Oreal.

202 Acupuncture began in China around 4500 years ago and involved piercing the skin with needles (back then, they were made of stone) in order to help the person's 'chi' (life force) flow more easily.

203 Aromatherapy is a method of alternative medicine and the concept has been around for a possible 9000 years! Many ancient civilizations, including the Egyptians, used aromatic oils and incense in the healing process.

204 It is likely that yoga as a meditative form is over 7000 years old. The principles of yoga are mentioned in the Hindu scriptures, the Upanishads, which date back over 3000 years.

205 Karate is a form of martial arts invented by the Chinese. The name 'Karate-do' translates to 'the way of the open hand'.

206 Judo is not only a martial art, but also a philosophy that comes from the Japanese culture. Its founder was Kano Jigoro towards the end of the nineteenth century.

207 Wilhelm Conrad Rontgen discovered X-rays in 1895 when he found an image had been cast by his cathode ray generator. He took the first X-ray photograph . . . of his wife's hand!

208 MRI stands for magnetic resonance imaging and is a method of seeing inside the body for medical purposes. Raymond Damadian invented the first MRI scanner in 1970.

209 Godfrey Hounsfield and Allan Cormack were individually working on the idea of the CAT-scan during 1972. In 1975, X-ray technology helped Robert Ledley to patent the CAT-scan machine, which can take 3D X-rays.

210 In 1853, two scientists, Charles Gabriel Prevaz and Alexander Wood, came up with a syringe that could safely pierce the skin of a human. Injections and infusions had been around since 1670; this was the first hypodermic syringe.

211 Aspirin was a discovery by Felix Hoffman in 1899 when he saw that his father used salicylic acid, the ingredient in aspirin, to help his rheumatism.

212 In 1865, Joseph Lister found that cleaning an operating theater with carbolic acid helped maintain a sterilized area. This was the forerunner of antiseptic.

213 The first hospital for the public was probably built around the end of the fourth century in Rome. It was the idea of a woman who would eventually be made a saint. St Fabiola went on to build many more hospitals.

214 Spectacles have a debatable history. Some say the use of magnifying lenses for improved sight may date back to the Chinese in the tenth century, but the actual eyewear itself may not have come into existence until the end of the thirteenth century.

215 Bifocal spectacles were invented by Benjamin Franklin. In his later years he had difficulty using his reading glasses for everyday use, so he invented a double lens pair of spectacles through which he could read when looking down and see distances when looking straight ahead.

216 Toothpaste was around in the nineteenth century and was bought by the jar. A dentist named Washington Sheffield first had the idea to market it in a tube but it was William Colgate's dental cream that would surpass it in 1896.

217 Nitrous oxide, or 'laughing gas' as it is more commonly known, was discovered by Humphrey Davy in 1799. Although it would later be used in the surgery, Davy also made his parties more entertaining (and dangerous) by making his guests laugh.

18 The stethoscope was invented by Rene Laennec in 1819 simply because he was too embarrassed to place his ear so close to a stranger's chest!

19 Two French chemists named Joseph Caventou and Pierre Pelletier were responsible for discovering quinine, which was useful when treating malaria. They also discovered the anaesthetic alcohol, chloroform.

220 Louis Pasteur was the man who, in 1865, realized that living organisms within foodstuffs could cause disease. His process of destroying the organisms was called pasteurization.

21 Louis Pasteur also came up with the vaccination for rabies in 1885. Long before this, there were myths about how to cure people who had been bitten by a rabid dog. One was to chew the hair of the dog that bit you. This didn't work but gave us the saying, 'The hair of the dog'.

22 Thermometers for medical use were introduced in 1866. They were smaller and easier to handle than the usual domestic thermometer.

223 Continuing the theme of sterilization, William Halsted from the US invented extremely thin, yet strong, rubber gloves to wear when performing surgery. These are still in use today.

224 To prevent infection from tetanus, two scientists named Emil Behring and Kitasato Shibasaburo came up with an immunisation. It was a heated or chemically treated poison from the original virus and acted as a vaccine.

225 Doctors use an instrument called a sphygmomanometer to measure blood pressure. An Italian, Scipione Riva-Rocci, invented this device in 1896.

226 Marie Curie was the first female Doctor of Science in Europe. Most of her work was shared with her husband, Pierre, until his death in 1906. Through her work and research into radiotherapy, she also became the first woman to win the Nobel Prize in 1903. She won a second in 1910.

227 In 1901 an Austrian named Karl Landsteiner discovered that there were different types of blood groups and that mixing the wrong sorts during a transfusion could actually kill a patient.

228 Johnson & Johnson employee Earle Dickson in the USA made self-adhesive dressings in 1920 by placing pieces of gauze onto sticky tape. He then rolled them up and sold them as Band-aids®.

229 Insulin is used to control diabetes and was discovered by Frederick Banting and Charles Best in 1921.

230 Fred Sanger and Dorothy Hodgkin discovered the structure of insulin in 1969. This important breakthrough helped scientists form a synthetic variety.

231 The iron lung was an invention by Phillip Drinker and Louis Agassiz Shaw in 1927. The original design was operated using a couple of vacuum cleaners and a large, iron-sided casket.

232 The pacemaker is a life-saving device that uses electrical impulses to keep a patient's heart beating. An early design in 1952 by Paul Zoll was too heavy to move around, so in 1957 Earl Bakken designed a smaller battery-powered one.

This is the best artificial heart we can give you in 1952, Mr Smith. But don't worry about its size. It fits nicely onto a small trailer you can tow behind you wherever you go.

CHUGGA CHUGGA PUMP PUMP

233 In 1998, Brandon Whale, aged ten, invented a device called the Pace Mate. This was an elasticized version of the sensor-bracelet worn by his mother after she had a pacemaker fitted. By adding electrolyte sponges that helped to conduct the electricity, Brandon's mother was able to send her electrocardiogram readings effectively to the hospital monitoring her.

234 Brandon wasn't the only inventor in his family. His brother, Spencer, who was three years younger, noticed how, when children in hospitals rode around in toy cars, their IV drips would have to be carried behind by desperate parents. Spencer designed a toy car that incorporated the drip, so the parents wouldn't have to chase around after them.

235 The heart-lung machine is a device that replaces the heart's function during surgery. It was invented by John Gibbon Jr in 1953. Over the years vast improvements have been made, but his was the prototype.

236 The polio vaccine was invented by Jonas Salk in 1952 and, like other vaccines, contained the dead virus. The modern form of the polio vaccine was an improved version by Albert Sabin.

237 DNA, or deoxyribonucleic acid, is the core of life. Two men, Francis Crick and James Watson, were the ones who discovered the chemical structure of DNA in 1953.

What shall we call our newly discovered chemical structure, Francis? Something catchy like... Deoxyribonucleic Acid?

James, my friend. No one is going to be able to say that... let alone remember it. Just DNA will do old chap.

238 The very first heart transplant was done in 1967. The operation was performed by a surgeon from South Africa named Christiaan Barnard.

239 Genetic engineering once seemed like it was from the imagination of a science fiction author, but now there have been such major advances in technology that is possible to alter the DNA of an organism. Stanley Cohen and Herbert Boyer discovered the science in 1972.

We've altered its DNA. Amazing isn't it! Yesterday... that was a gold fish. Don't be fooled by its smile, either. I think it might bite!

A Dedicated Follower of Fashion

240 Trainers or sneakers were a sports shoe designed by Adolf Dasler in 1949, and were very popular with athletes.

241 The zipper was originally designed for shoes in 1893 by Whitcomb Judson from Chicago. An engineer from Sweden named Gideon Sundback improved the device by replacing the hooks in the fastener with teeth or cups locking together. The word 'zip' came from the boots on which these fasteners were placed—zippers!

242 The earliest shoes were simply leather sandals. The idea grew and in places like ancient Mesopotamia, feet were covered completely with the leather. Eventually, in Crete, boots were invented that went right up to the knee.

243 Before the invention of shoelaces in the early twentieth century, shoes were often fastened with buckles or buttons. Modern laces are often made of cotton. The small plastic bit on the end is called an 'aglet'.

244 The first underwear to be worn was most likely the loincloth. In the Middle Ages, men began to wear 'braies', short pantaloons that tied at the waist and above the knee. Women wore an undergarment called a 'shift'.

245 Socks have a mysterious background and little is known about when they first started being worn. It is estimated that it was 2000–3000 years ago.

246 Gloves were not always worn to keep people's hands warm in cold weather. Often, as with many garments, they were of ceremonial value. Gloves were discovered in the tomb of King Tutankhamen in Egypt.

247 Jacob Davis and Levi Strauss invented denim jeans during the gold rush of the 1840s and 50s, in America. They patented their idea in 1873 and it has now remained a staple in fashion, decade after decade.

248 Silk, from the silk worm, was discovered by the Chinese over 4500 years ago. It was one of the best-kept secrets in the fashion world for centuries!

249 Lipstick has been a part of the fashion world for as long as make-up has, but it was Maurice Levy in 1915 who revolutionized the accessory by placing it in a tube for portable use.

BEFORE LIPSTICK CAME IN A TUBE.

Dear, could you check my lipstick and tell me if I've smudged it? And do I look beautiful?

250 Cecil Gee, a tailor, designed the first buttoned shirt in 1932 due to public demand, as people were tired of pulling garments on over their heads!

251 The bikini was invented in 1946 by two rival fashion designers in France. They both came up with the two-piece swimsuit for women. One, designed by Jacques Heim, was called the Atome and the other, designed by Louis Reard, was called the Bikini.

252 Miniskirts were enormously popular in the liberated 1960s. They were designed by a French designer called André Courreges in 1964.

They call this a dress? That's a handkerchief!

THE MINISKIRT

253 Wigs have been around for a long time. Ancient Egyptians wore wigs for decorative purposes. They were often made of human hair attached to a net.

254 The young Max Factor was fascinated by concoctions and potions while he was an apprentice for a pharmacist. In due course, he opened a shop in Moscow selling make-up products and eventually moved to America in 1908. His products have gone on to be incredibly famous.

255 Perfume has been around for thousands of years. The earliest dates back to the ancient Egyptians, who often used it in religious ceremonies.

ERRRR! What's that smell? It smells like a dead hippopotamus lying in the sun on the banks of the Nile!

It's the Pharaoh's new aftershave 'Dead Hippo'! It's all the rage right now.

256 The first artificial hair dye was an invention by Eugene Schueller (the founder of L'Oreal) in 1907. Natural substances such as henna had been previously used.

Florence... You've just had your hair colored with that new invention... hair dye.

Does it come in any other color than green?

257 Watches were not originally designed as fashion items, but as a portable way to tell the time. Peter Henlein from Germany invented the first pocket watch in 1524, and it was as large as a fist. Over time, watches became smaller and various designs made them a fashion accessory—right up to the present day where we now wear them on our wrists!

258 Champagne is named after the region in France where it is made. It has been suggested that the first person to make this type of bubbly wine was the winemaker Dom Perignon, in 1670.

259 The corkscrew was invented around the same time as the use of corks to seal bottled wine in the late 1600s. It is said that the first corkscrews were tools with a spiral end, usually used for cleaning out the end of a musket gun!

260 The Coca-Cola® company was founded by the drinks inventor John Pemberton, in 1892. Coca-Cola® was originally so named because it contained cocaine and caffeine (which came from kola-nuts). The drink no longer contains cocaine.

261 Soup is 8000 years old. The word originally comes from the term to describe bread that has been soaked in meat juices— 'sop'.

262 Caesar salad was not invented by the great Julius Caesar, but rather by a Mexican named Caesar Gardini in the 1920s.

263 Chocolate was first used by the Olmec Indians, the Mayans, and the Aztecs. It was a drink made from the cocoa bean. The Aztecs called it 'xocalatl', which is the link to the modern word, 'chocolate'. This translates to 'warm and bitter liquid'.

264 The first chocolate bar was made by Joseph Fry & Son in 1847.

265 Joseph Priestley initiated fizzy drinks in 1772, after the naturally carbonated water found in springs inspired him.

266 Vitamins were an important discovery. Frederick Hopkins from England worked out that we needed more than just the carbohydrates, fats, and proteins in our diet and identified there was something else important in food. In 1912, a biochemist from Poland named Casimir Funk decided to call these bonus ingredients 'vitamines' after the amine found in rice.

267 Pizza has been around for centuries but the first pizza shop was opened in Naples, in 1830. This shop is still selling pizzas today!

268 It has been suggested that ice-cream has been around from as early as the time of Emperor Nero in the Roman period—around 57 AD.

269 The hamburger has its origins in Germany. When German immigrants went to the USA, they took their concept of meat patties in a sandwich or roll with them.

270 Hot dogs were also from Germany. Germans are renowned for their various sausages and it was easier to eat them when wrapped in a blanket of bread or a roll. It is suspected that the term 'hot dog' comes from the similarity of the sausage to a Dachshund 'sausage' dog.

271 The sandwich is named after the Earl of Sandwich, who invented it in the middle of the eighteenth century. He was extremely fond of eating meat placed between two slices of toast.

272 Tomato ketchup was first made by the Heinz Company in 1876. The word 'ketchup' comes from a Chinese word 'ke-tsiap', which is a type of pickled fish dressing.

273 Forrest Mars created M&Ms inspired by the soldiers in the Spanish Civil War, who were eating sugar-coated lumps of chocolate.

274 Coffee dates back to about 800 BC, but it is likely it was being drunk for a long time before then. Surprisingly, the Western world has only been drinking it for about three hundred years.

275 The doughnut/donut with a hole was invented by Captain Hanson Crockett Gregory in the 1840s, but it was William Rosenberg who opened up the first 'Dunkin' Donut' chain in 1948 in the USA.

276 Pasta is, surprisingly, not an Italian invention but Chinese. It dates back over 4000 years!

277 Pretzels are fifteen centuries old and have been a popular snack for fasting Christians and Jews, as the ingredients are merely flour and water. It is said the form of the pretzel represents the holy trinity.

278 Sushi is a Japanese invention and although most believe the term relates to the raw fish, it actually refers to the use of sushi rice (seasoned with vinegar).

279 Bubblegum was invented in 1928 by Walter Diemer, when he was working at a chewing gum factory.

280 Will Keith Kellogg invented corn flakes in 1894 when he was researching a healthy diet for hospital patients.

281 Frank Epperson invented the ice lolly or popsicle, and he patented the idea in 1924.

282 The first robot was invented around 370 BC! Archytas of Tarentum, Greece, was a scientist who fashioned a pigeon out of wood. His wooden robot bird moved like a flying bird when rotated on a steam-powered arm.

283 Clocks have come in many forms, from the sundial to the digital, but the first mechanical clock was designed by Su Sung in 1088. It was a waterwheel that would repeatedly fill a bucket of water and then empty it in a steady clockwork fashion.

284 In 1335, the first chiming clock was created in Milan in Italy. It would sound every hour.

DANG DANG DANG

Oh-a boy! Like-a I don't-a know it's-a three o'clock. This clock-a tell-a me-a what-a time it is-a every hour!

285 The Hamilton Watch Company made a prototype pulsar digital watch in 1970. Two years later it was on the market, with a light-emitting diode display.

What do you think of my new space age watch with a light-emitting diode display?

But it's got no hands! How are you going to tell the time?

1970s THINKING!

286 The barometer, named in 1676 by Edme Mariotte, was invented by a friend of Galileo's called Evangelista Torricelli. Mercury within a calibrated tube rose and fell depending on the air pressure outside.

287 The Celsius scale was invented by Anders Celsius in 1742 when he was frustrated with the oddly placed numbers in the Fahrenheit scale. He preferred to go decimal but, strangely, decided to make 100 degrees the freezing point and 0 the boiling point. This was eventually inverted.

I'm not too keen on Mr Fahrenheit's scale. I think I'll make my own. Where's my quill?

288 Porcelain is a fine yet strong type of pottery, and is made when the ingredients are heated to a point where they become glasslike. The Chinese were behind its creation around 800 AD.

289 Photography had its beginnings in 1826 when Nicephore Niepce from France placed a sheet of metal coated in tar into a box with a glass lens window in one side. After a few hours, the sunlight had penetrated the lens and left an image on the tarred metal, producing the first photograph!

290 In 1888, an American businessman named George Eastman founded the Kodak Camera Company. The cameras came with film inside them and when you had finished the roll, you returned the camera to the company, which would develop the film for you.

291 Black and white pictures were printed using a process called 'half-tone', which was invented by Max and Louis Levy in 1890.

292 The first examples of holography (3D projections) were created in 1948, and were a brainwave of Dennis Gabor from Hungary. Interestingly, his concept came before the invention of the laser, which is the tool used to make holograms these days.

293 In 1931, Harold Edgerton created the flash for a camera by using xenon gas and a high voltage pulse.

294 LASER stands for light amplification by simulated emission of radiation. The concept was discovered in 1958 by two physicists, Charles Townes and Arthur Schawlow.

295 Streetlamps were first invented by the Romans in 50 AD. The lamps were not very bright, as they were only fueled by oil.

GLUTIUS MAXIMUS ARRIVES HOME IN ROME AFTER FIVE YEARS IN GAUL FIGHTING THE BARBARIANS.

296 Swedish man Alfred Nobel invented dynamite in 1867. His fame and fortune led him to institute the Nobel Prize.

297 The windmill was an extension of the waterwheel in many respects. Wind drove the windmill's sails, which drove a millstone to grind wheat and corn. Even though windmills were around in 600 AD, they remain useful up to the present day, when they can now generate electricity.

298 The Chinese were the first people to discover gunpowder over a thousand years ago by mixing three ingredients together to make an explosive. Originally intended for amusement and fireworks, gunpowder would also be used for military purposes.

299 The microscope is an instrument that combines lenses together in order to magnify the smallest object. Hans Janssen was the first to attempt to make a microscope, in 1600 in Holland.

300 Alessandro Volta from Italy invented the first battery in 1800, using silver and zinc. His invention was inspired by his friend Luigi Galvini, who had noticed a dead frog's muscles would spasm when in contact with two different metals.

301 The lead-acid battery still in use in cars today was invented by the Frenchman Gaston Plante, in 1859.

302 The first calculator was simply called an adding machine, and was designed by Thomas de Colmar in 1820. Sadly, because he was an insurance man and not an engineer, it didn't work to the standard he desired. Other inventors would make improvements to it over the next thirty years.

303 In 1885, William Burroughs invented the adder-lister, which printed out the calculations it made.

304 RADAR (radio detection and ranging) was invented by Robert Watson-Watt in 1935 as a way of detecting enemy aircraft.

305 The Richter scale measures seismic tremors and earthquakes. It was invented by Charles Richter and Beno Gutenberg in 1935.

306 The first nuclear reactor was created inside a squash court in a university in Chicago by Enrico Fermi in 1942.

307 In 1941, an American scientist named Russell Ohl discovered the wonders of solar power while working with impure silicon.

308 The world of science needed a system of measurements that everyone could use so as not to complicate matters. A system known as the Systeme Internationale d'Unites (or 'SI' for short) was implemented by the eleventh General Conference on Weights and Measures in 1960.

309 The transistor is an essential part of all electronics, as it has the ability to control the electricity inside them. In 1947, the first one was invented by three men, William Shockley, Walter Brattain, and John Bardeen.

310 In 1940, Claude Shannon established that the work of 19th century mathematician George Boole could be applied to electronic circuits, providing the foundations of digital logic upon which all computers rely.

311 Early computer designs as far back as 1940 were using binary coding thanks to John Atanasoff and Clifford Berry. Binary coding is made up of only 1s and 0s.

312 The first computer to use all electronics rather than mechanics was invented in 1945 by John Propser Eckert and John Mauchley. It was, however, an enormous machine and was superseded later by more practical designs.

313 The memory of a computer is very important, as it is where programs are stored. It is likely that the first computer memory was designed by John von Neumann in Hungary.

314 If it wasn't for the error-correcting code invented by Richard Hamming in 1950, many machines like mobile phones would not work today!

315 The first mini computer was not as 'mini' as we would think of in today's computer age, but it was certainly smaller than the computers that could fill a room. In 1965 Kenneth Olsen from America reduced the size by using the integrated circuit system and it took off around the world.

316 The first floppy disks were large 20-centimeter (8-inch) square disks that could contain data. They were invented by the IBM group in 1970. The smaller and decidedly less floppy versions were introduced by Sony in 1980.

317 Calculators had been around for some time when, in the 1970s, it was decided to design smaller and more portable models. Various scientists including Jack Kilby, James Van Tassel, and Jerry Merryman attempted the pocket calculator. The British inventor Clive Sinclair (later knighted) drew on technology advances for his version, which became vastly popular.

What's the square root of 365 plus 2,400 multiplied by .0058?

Just give me a sec!

IN THE 1970s BEFORE EVERYONE HAD MOBILE PHONES...THEY ALL HAD CALCULATORS.

318 The personal computer was first produced in 1977. Three famous examples are the Tandy®, the Commodore®, and the Apple®. The men behind the last, Steve Jobs and Stephen Wozniak, were great promoters and their model took off as the leading computer of the time.

Hey Steve! What are we going to call our computer company? Oh...would you like some apple...? I've already eaten half.

Some apple? Now Stephen... There's an idea!

319 BASIC computer code was devised for the beginner of computers. It was written by John Kemeny and Tom Kurtz in 1963.

320 The Internet was first considered in 1962 when J. C. R. Licklider thought of networking various computers. In 1969 this was developed into a system called ARPANET. By 1970, new technology made it possible to transfer data from machine to machine. More machines were added to the network and by the 1980s technology allowed the spread of the Internet across the world.

321 The World Wide Web was invented by British physicist Tim Berners-Lee in 1990, when he designed the hypertext software used in web browsers.

322 Until 1993, the World Wide Web was unable to mix text and graphics. Then twenty-one-year-old Marc Andreessen invented 'Mosaic', the first graphical browser, which lead to the development of Netscape and Internet Explorer.

323 The Windows® operating system was an invention from the minds at the Microsoft Corporation in 1985.

324 The very first cloned animal was the famous Dolly the Sheep. She was the product of genetic engineering by British scientists Ian Wilmut and Keith Campbell in 1996.

325 One of the most important advantages of cloning could be the possibility of helping endangered animals survive. Philip Damiani from Iowa, in the USA, managed to clone the endangered member of the ox family known as the gaur in 2001. The cloned animal, named Noah, gave hope of other animals being saved from extinction.

326 Numbers have been around for centuries, but the modern numeric system comes from an Arabic form, which was deciphered by Leonardo Pisano in 1202 and used the system of tens and units.

327 The French introduced the metric system in 1789 after the French Revolution, as it was felt to be more practical and logical.

Ahh! Theese new Metreek seestem is...how do you say... confusing. I don't know ten kilo of gurn powder from three metres of rope!

THE NEW METRIC SYSTEM ARRIVES IN FRANCE IN 1789.

328 Rockets for space travel were a fantastical dream for many years. There were three men who made the dream into a reality in their own separate professional fields. Robert Goddard (USA), Hermann Oberth (Germany), and Konstantin Eduodovich Tsiolkovsky (Russia) each researched liquid powered rockets in the 1920s.

329 Of course, smaller rockets were much simpler and were made by the Chinese following their inventions of gunpowder and fireworks. In approximately 1300, these fireworks were no longer purely for enjoyment, but were employed as weapons when attached to arrows!

What does the note say Chen?

It says... You have 10 seconds to big bang!

CHINESE WARFARE 1300s STYLE.

330 Space suits were invented out of necessity and were designed by a number of people working for the space program, both in America and Russia. Astronauts needed something to wear that would protect them from pressure in the vacuum of space and from the freezing temperatures.

331 The telescope was invented in 1608 by a Dutch spectacle maker called Hans Lippershey. He noticed that when he looked through two parallel lenses, objects would appear bigger.

332 The Russians launched the first artificial satellite in 1957. It was made by Valentin Glushko and Sergey Korolyuov, and was named Sputnik 1.

333 Space flight was a landmark event in humankind's history. Yuri Gagarin from Russia was the very first human being to orbit the Earth, in 1961.

334 The first space station was a team effort from the people at NASA. There was an attempt in 1971 by the Russians, but sadly, it crashed to Earth within half a year. Skylab was NASA's station. It was launched in 1973 and stayed in space until 1979.

335 The space shuttle was another NASA success story. Launched in 1981, it journeyed for fifty-four hours before returning to Earth and landing in a similar way to a plane.

Captain! Was that what I thought it was? A 747?

Captain! Was that what I thought it was? The Space Shuttle?

THE SPACE SHUTTLE THINKS IT'S A PLANE.

336 The umbrella was originally used as a sun shade. The Chinese and Japanese had lightweight parasols for this purpose. Samuel Fox invented the steel-framed waterproof umbrella in 1874. Not surprisingly, he was from England!

COOL
PRACTICAL
JOKES

COOL PRACTICAL JOKES

Playing practical jokes is great fun. Part of the fun comes from planning the joke and the rest comes from seeing the joke work. However, there are two things that you must remember when carrying out your practical jokes:

* Practical jokes should never hurt anyone.
* Practical jokes should never be cruel.

This section has heaps of cool practical jokes, each broken up in two sections: the sting and the set-up. The sting explains what will happen to the victim of the joke. The set-up explains how to set up and carry out the joke.

One more thing to remember: when playing a practical joke, your victim will often seek revenge. Don't play any jokes unless you are willing to take them as well!

Contents

No Joke

Practical 1

This practical joke involves not playing a practical joke, which makes it a very good practical joke indeed. Does that make sense?

The Sting

It is traditional to play practical jokes on people on 1 April—April Fool's Day. April Fool's Day is approaching. Every year, you have played a practical joke on a particular victim. This year, the victim again expects to have a practical joke played on them. You remind them that April Fool's Day is approaching and they start getting worried. On the morning of April Fool's Day, they wake up in a sweat, dreading what's going to happen today. Until midday, when April Fool's Day officially ends, they cannot relax for a second. When midday passes, they breathe a big sigh of relief because they haven't been a victim of a practical joke. At least that's what they think. The fact that you didn't play a practical joke was a joke in itself because you had them so worried.

What You Need: nothing, just a victim

The Set-up

1 As April Fool's Day approaches, pick a victim who would expect you to play a joke on them.

2 Every day, remind them how many days it is until April Fool's Day.

3 Tell them that you have a really big practical joke planned for them this year.

4 The day before April Fool's Day, walk past them rubbing your hands together, as if you are getting really excited about the joke you are going to play the following day.

5 On the morning of April Fool's Day, walk past them several times and chuckle or give them a grin. This will make them feel even more uncomfortable.

6 At one minute to midday on April Fool's Day, walk up to the victim and say 'April Fool'.

7 When the victim reminds you that April Fool's Day ends in one minute and that you have not played a joke on them, tell them that you've been playing the joke all morning. Explain that the joke was the fact you didn't play a joke, but you still managed to have them running scared.

The Disappearing Money

Everyone loves finding money in the street. Particularly when the money is a bill. This joke gets people excited about finding money. The problem is, they can't grab hold of it.

The Sting

The victim of the joke is walking down the street. They notice a piece of paper in the middle of the sidewalk. It looks like money but they can't be sure from a distance. As they get closer, they realize that they're right. They can't believe their luck. They think about what they're going to buy with the money. They bend down to pick it up. Just before they grab it, it skips away. Even if they chase the money, it keeps skipping away every time they get close to it.

What You Need: a money bill; some fishing line; a large bush, tree, fence or wall to hide behind

The Set-up

1. Make a tiny hole in the bill and thread some fishing line through it.

2. Pick a place where there is a bush, tree, fence, or wall that you can hide behind. Make sure that you have a good view of the sidewalk, but that people walking along the sidewalk cannot see you.

3. When no one is coming, place the bill on the sidewalk, then hide.

4. Hold the end of the fishing line and wait for a victim.

5. When someone bends down to pick up your bill, jerk the fishing line so that the bill moves away from the victim.

6. Keep doing this for as long as the person chases the bill.

Set-up Tip

You have to be very alert while you're doing this joke. Otherwise you may lose your money. Apart from running the risk of someone picking the bill up before you have time to jerk the fishing line, you have to watch out for people using a foot to trap the money. If they stamp on the bill before you pull the line, the bill will stay under their shoe. Then you'll be the victim.

Similar Joke

A similar joke can be done with a coin. Instead of using fishing line, use extra-strength glue to stick the coin to the sidewalk. Then stand back and watch people struggle to pick it free. The only problem with this joke is that you won't get your coin back.

This joke will frustrate your victim. It is especially good to play this joke on people who are particular about the way they organize their CD collection.

The Sting

The victim goes to put on one of their favorite CDs. They turn the CD player on, take the CD out of its cover and put it in the player. They press the 'Play' button and get a shock when the music that plays is not what they expected. They take the CD out and check the label. It does not match the cover. They grab another CD from their collection and look inside. This one is also wrong. They go through their entire collection and every single CD has been swapped around.

> **What You Need: the victim's CD collection; about half an hour to do the swapping**

The Set-up

1 Make sure the victim is occupied elsewhere for at least half an hour.

2 Stack the CD covers into one large pile. Do not take the CDs out of their covers yet.

3 Open the top CD cover and take the CD out. Open the second CD cover and take the CD out. Place the first CD into the second CD cover.

4 Open the third CD cover and take the CD out. Place the second CD into the third CD cover.

5 Repeat this process right to the bottom of the pile. The last CD will go in the top CD cover. (The reason for swapping the CDs in such an organized manner is to ensure that no CD is put back into its own cover.)

6 Put the CDs back where you got them from. If the victim always has their CDs in a certain order, make sure that you put them back in the same order. Otherwise they'll suspect someone has touched them.

Similar Jokes

• You can also play this joke with people's video collections and vinyl record collections.

• You can swap people's books around by swapping the dust covers on their books. To make things even worse for the victim, put some of the dust covers on upside down.

Practical

'Look, Up in the Sky'

4

This joke costs nothing, needs no equipment, and can have many victims. That makes it a very good practical joke to play.

The Sting

A crowd of people is gathered at the bottom of a tall building. Everyone is looking up at the top of the building. Some of the people start whispering and asking each other what is going on. Over the next few minutes, the crowd grows bigger and bigger. Rumors start spreading that someone is out on the roof of the building. After about ten minutes, the crowd has become so large that it is holding up traffic. A police officer comes along and tells the crowd to move away. Eventually, the crowd does move away. Many of them watch the television news that night to see if anything dramatic happened. Of course, the incident doesn't make it to the news because nothing did happen. It was all a practical joke started by you.

What You Need: a tall building in a busy street; a couple of volunteers

The Set-up

1 Pick a tall building in a busy street.

2 When there are quite a few people walking past, stand at the bottom of the building and look up at the top.

3 Have one of your friends walk past and stop near you. You have to act as if you don't know each other. Your friend should also look up.

4 Have another friend walk past and stop. Again, you should all act as if you don't know each other. One of you should point towards the top of the building and whisper something to the others.

5 By now, you should have aroused the interest of people passing by.

6 As the crowd of people grows, you and your friends should walk away and watch from somewhere else.

Similar Jokes
• If you are on a crowded beach, look at the sea and point out into the distance.
• If you are at a sporting event, stand up and look at a point several rows behind you.
• If you are in the classroom, look out of the window and point into the distance.

Have you ever had the urge to move all the furniture in your bedroom, just for a change? Well, it's much more fun if you do it in a friend's room—without them knowing.

The Sting

The victim goes to their bedroom after being away for the day. They open the bedroom door and cannot believe their eyes. Their bed is where the desk usually is, and the desk is where the bed usually is. The posters that were on the walls are now on the ceiling, and the rug from the floor is hanging over the curtain rod. The clothes that were hanging in the wardrobe have been squashed into the chest of drawers, and the socks, underpants, and handkerchiefs that were in the chest of drawers are now on hangers in the wardrobe.

What You Need: a friend's bedroom; some friends to help you; about half a day

The Set-up

1 Get permission from the victim's parents to change the victim's bedroom around. (You will probably have to promise to help the victim put everything back where it was.)

2 Find out when the victim will be away from home for a few hours.

3 Make a plan at least a day before the joke. Draw a map of the victim's bedroom and work out where you are going to put everything.

4 Write down the order in which you are going to move things. This will make things much easier on the day.

5 On the day of the joke, start work as soon as the victim leaves home. You may need all the time you can get.

6 Make sure you have a few friends to help you lift and move the items around.

7 When you have finished, leave a note on the bed with a message for the victim to work out. It could be the name of a furniture-moving service made up of the first letters of the names of everyone who helped play the joke.

Safety Tip
Lifting heavy objects can cause injuries. When you lift anything heavy, make sure that you bend your knees and pick the object up from the bottom. This should help avoid painful back injuries.

Not So Quick and Easy Jokes

Practical 6

Holiday Snaps

This joke takes some organizing but it is very funny. Some people use garden gnomes to play this joke, but you can use your victim's favorite toy or other item.

The Sting

The victim gets an envelope in the mail. They open it up and inside is a photograph of their favorite teddy bear at the airport. On the back of the photo is a note saying 'You never take me anywhere, so I've gone on a trip by myself'. The victim races up to their room to look for their teddy bear. They can't find it anywhere. Over the next few weeks,

they receive lots of photos of their teddy bear at various holiday destinations. One morning, just as they begin to wonder whether they will ever see their teddy bear again, they open the front door to find their teddy bear on the doormat. The bear is holding a note saying 'I'm back. Did you miss me?'.

What You Need: a toy or favorite item from the victim; a camera; envelopes; stamps; someone going on vacation

The Set-up

1. Find someone who is going on a vacation and is willing to help you play this joke. If you are going on vacation, you can do it yourself, but the victim may guess that you're playing a practical joke on them. It is best if the victim does not know the person on vacation.

2. Sneak one of the victim's favorite toys out of their room. Don't worry, they will get it back. A doll, teddy bear, or other soft toy is best.

3. Give the toy to the person going away.

4. Also give them your victim's address and a few envelopes. If the person is having a vacation within your country, you can give them the stamps they'll need. If the person is going overseas, they will have to buy the stamps themselves. You can give them some money to pay for the stamps.

5. Instruct the person going on vacation to position the toy in front of famous landmarks and take photos of the toy.

6. They should then write a message on the back of each photo and send the photos to the victim.

7. When the person returns from vacation, get the toy back and place it outside the victim's front door.

The Holey Cup Practical

7

Watch the victim's frustration as they try their best to quench their thirst—only to end up with the contents of their drink down the front of their shirt.

The Sting

The victim of the joke gets ready to drink something delicious. Imagine how frustrated they get when the liquid leaks out of the cup and onto their clothes before it reaches their mouth.

I would have enjoyed that drink... if my shirt hadn't drunk it all first!

What You Need: a plastic cup; a pin; a tasty drink; a cloth

The Set-up

1 Use the pin to prick some holes just below the rim of the cup.

2 Tempt the victim with the offer of a tasty drink.

3 Pour the drink, but make sure that the liquid remains below the pinholes.

4 Give the victim the drink.

5 Watch as the drink spurts out of the holes before it can reach the victim's mouth.

6 Use the cloth to help the victim clean themselves up.

What's delicious wet, cold...and all over somebody's shirt?

THIS DRINK!!

Set-up Tips
• Make sure that the holes in the cup are large enough for liquid to flow through but small enough so that the victim cannot see them.
• Practice the joke with water before your victim is at your house. That way you can make sure the holes are exactly the right size.
• Know what your victim's favorite drink is. That way they'll find your offer of a drink hard to refuse.

Food and Drink Jokes

The Holey Straw

This practical joke is similar to the Holey Cup joke, except that it is a straw that causes the problem.

The Sting

Like the Holey Cup joke, the victim of the joke gets ready to drink something delicious. This time, their frustration comes about because they cannot suck any liquid up through their straw. No matter how hard they suck on the straw, all that happens is their face gets redder and redder.

The Set-up

1 Use the pin to prick two holes near the bottom of the straw and two more near the top of the straw. The holes should be opposite each other.

What You Need: a straw; a pin; a cap or can of tasty drink

3 Watch as they try to suck the drink up through the straw. The holes make it virtually impossible for liquid to make its way up the straw.

2 Give the victim the drink. It is best if it is a drink that you know they like. That way they'll find it hard to refuse.

4 Encourage the victim to suck harder. Then enjoy the discomfort they are experiencing.

Follow-up

You could have a second holey straw handy. Then you could tell the victim that there must be something wrong with the first straw and offer them the replacement. Watch with delight as they struggle again.

The Knotty Straw

Here's another joke involving a straw. Like the Holey Straw joke, the victim will suck and suck and never get anywhere. For this joke to work, the victim has to have a cup with a lid on it, like the sort served in fast-food outlets.

The Sting

The victim of the joke eats some of their food and gets ready to take a drink. They start sucking on their straw but nothing happens. They suck harder and harder, but still nothing comes out. Meanwhile, everyone at the table is laughing at the victim's attempts to have a drink.

The Set-up

What You Need: a cup of drink—the cup must have a lid; a straw; a few seconds to prepare the joke

1 Next time you're at a fast-food outlet, pick out a friend to do the trick on.

2 Make sure that your friend buys a drink.

3 If they do not want a drink, offer to buy one for them. They'll find your offer hard to refuse.

4 Now you need to be alone with the drink for a few seconds. Offer to carry their drink to the table for them.

5 Get to the table as fast as you can and pull the lid off the drink. Take the straw out and tie a knot in the middle.

6 Put the straw and lid back before the victim gets to the table. The knot in the straw will stop any drink getting to their mouth.

7 If the victim insists on carrying their drink, wait until they go to the bathroom or arrange for someone to distract them.

Sausage Fingers

Practical 10

This joke will scare the pants off the victim. They'll probably run to the phone to call an ambulance before they realize that it's a joke.

The Sting

The victim of the joke shakes your hand. They get the shock of their life when you pull your hand away and scream. They are left holding what they think is one of your fingers. It turns out to be a sausage.

> How do you do young man? Is that a sausage with sauce on the end.. or is that... aahhrr... A FINGER THAT FELL OFF??

What You Need: a sausage (the color of the sausage should be as close to that of your skin as possible); knife; ketchup or tomato sauce (optional)

The Set-up

1 Buy a sausage that is very close to the color of your skin. It should also be skinny.

2 Trim the sausage so that it is about the same length as one of your fingers. Be very careful when using a knife to trim the sausage.

3 Just before meeting the victim, place the sausage between two of your fingers.

4 As the victim approaches, get ready to greet them but don't put your hand out too soon. You don't want them seeing six fingers on your hand or they may get suspicious.

5 At the very last moment, put out your hand for them to shake.

6 Shake hands, then pull your hand away, leaving them holding the sausage. Then scream as though in pain.

> Those big fat barbecue sausages look just like fingers. I'd like to try one on for size please! If it fits.. how much for just ONE?

Follow-up
You can add to the joke by placing ketchup on the fingers that the sausage is between. The ketchup will look like blood.

Food and Drink Jokes

Practical 11

Sugar and Salt

This is one of the oldest jokes around. It's an easy way to play havoc with someone's taste buds.

The Sting

The victim sits down to a nice hot cup of coffee. They've been working hard and looking forward to this drink all day. They grab the sugar container and pour sugar into their cup. They then stir the liquid and take a sip. Imagine their horror when their coffee tastes of salt instead of sugar.

The Set-up

What You Need; a sugar container; a salt container; two saucers

1. Grab the salt and sugar containers at your victim's house.
2. Place the two saucers in front of you.

3. Pour the contents of the sugar container onto one saucer.
4. Pour the contents of the salt container onto the other saucer.
5. Pour the sugar from the saucer into the salt container.

6. Pour the salt from the saucer into the sugar container.
7. Put the containers back where you found them.

8. Try and be there when the victim gets a taste sensation they are not expecting.
9. This is a particularly good joke to play in a school cafeteria. Tell a few of your friends what you have done and have a laugh together as someone pours the wrong substance on their food or in their drink.

Practical 12

Movie Munchies

This joke may seem a little bit revolting, but you actually don't do anything revolting at all. It's all about planting an idea in the victim's mind.

The Sting

The victim, a friend of yours, is sitting at the movies. The advertisements and trailers have just finished and the main feature is about to start. The lights go out. You offer the victim a box of Maltesers, saying you are too full to finish them. The victim accepts and eats one of them. You then say something that makes the victim think twice about eating the rest of the Maltesers. It also spoils their enjoyment of the film. What is it that you say? Read the Set-up to find out.

The Set-up

What You Need; a movie theatre; a box of Maltesers, Jaffas, Junior Mints or other round, smooth candy

1. Make sure you are sitting next to the victim in the movie theatre.
2. When the lights are completely out, hand over an opened box of Maltesers, Jaffas, Junior Mints or other round, smooth candy.
3. Tell the victim that you are too full to eat them.

4. Wait until the victim has eaten a piece or two of the candy and then say to the victim, 'By the way, I put one of the candies up my nose and then put it back in the box'.

5. You haven't really put a piece of candy up your nose but the victim doesn't know this. They have to decide whether to believe you or not.
6. As the victim has already eaten a couple of pieces, they will probably feel sick thinking that one of them could have been up your nose.
7. If they decide to eat the rest of the box, they will feel very uneasy throughout the movie. It is amazing how slimy that candy feels when you have been told that one of them has been up someone's nose.

Salt and Pepper

Practical 13

Like the Sugar and Salt practical joke, this joke tricks people into shaking the wrong seasoning onto their food.

The Sting

The victim sits down to dinner. They taste their meal and decide that they need a little bit of salt. They grab the salt container and start shaking. To their amazement, pepper starts coming out. They take another look at the container, but it definitely contains salt. They can see the salt through the glass. They shake again. Still, pepper comes out. They grab the pepper container and start shaking. Salt comes out. They finally got what they wanted, but they have no idea why there is salt coming out of the pepper container and pepper coming out of the salt container.

I think my dinner needs a little more SALT... or is it PEPPER? No... it's SALT... hang on! So if there's PEPPER in the SALT... what's in my TEA? ...COFFEE?

What You Need: see-through salt and pepper containers; a paper napkin or wax paper; a pair of scissors

The Set-up

1 Make sure that the salt and pepper containers you are going to use are see-through. This means that the salt and pepper must be visible from the outside.

2 The containers must also have screw-top lids.

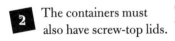

(A)

3 Unscrew the lids and turn the lids upside down on a table.

4 Pour some pepper into one of the upturned lids.

5 Pour some salt into the other upturned lid.

salt lid

Pepper lid

(B)

6 Cut out two pieces of the napkin or wax paper.

7 Place one of the pieces of paper on top of the salt in the upturned lid and press it so that the salt cannot fall out.

8 Place the other piece of paper on top of the pepper in the upturned lid and press it so that the pepper cannot fall out.

9 Screw the lid with salt onto the pepper container, then screw the lid with pepper onto the salt container. The victim will see salt in a container but, when they shake it, pepper will come out. The opposite will occur with the pepper container.

(C)

An Odd Vintage

Some wine drinkers are very fussy about the quality of the wine they drink. This joke is aimed at adults who think they know a lot about wine.

Oh my! What was the chicken eating when it layed these eggs..?

GRAPES

The Sting

Your victim is sitting down for dinner. You offer to get them a glass of wine. You fetch their wineglass and place it in front of them. You then fetch an egg-carton. Your victim is wondering what you're doing. They are in a state of shock when you pull an egg out, crack it on the edge of their glass, and split it in two. An egg-full of wine pours into their glass.

What You Need; an egg; some wine; a pin; a bowl; water; glue; a beaker

The Set-up

1 Using the pin, prick a tiny hole at each end of the eggshell.

2 Put one end of the eggshell to your mouth and blow as hard as you can. It will take some effort, but eventually you'll manage to blow all of the egg out.

3 Make sure that the egg falls into a bowl, not onto a table or the floor. You can then keep the egg for cooking.

4 Run some water through the empty shell. This washes the insides out. Repeat this several times.

5 Glue up one of the holes.

6 Carefully pour some wine into the remaining hole. This will take some time and a steady hand. You'll probably have to pour the wine into a beaker first.

7 When the eggshell is full, glue up the remaining hole. You are now ready to play the joke.

Similar Joke

Rather than fill the eggshell up with wine, you could fill it up with water and return it to its carton. Imagine the shock someone will get next time they go to make an omelet or boil an egg.

Sliced Banana

This is a very clever joke that will leave the victim baffled.

The Sting

The victim grabs a banana from their fruit bowl. They snap open the peel at the top, then peel the sides. They can't believe what they see inside. The banana has been cut into slices, all the way down. It looks ready to go into a fruit salad. They have no idea how this happened, and if you don't tell them, they never will.

What You Need: a banana; a needle; a victim who likes eating bananas

The Set-up

1 Pick a banana with a firm skin.

2 Take the needle and poke it through the banana skin, near the top.

3 Wiggle the needle from side to side. This action slices the banana.

4 Take the needle out and poke it back in the banana skin a little further down.

5 Repeat the wiggling action.

6 Do the same in several places all the way down the banana.

7 When you have finished, put the banana at the top of the fruit bowl. Then wait for a victim to come along.

Follow-up

If you are near the victim when they peel the banana, tell them that you heard on the radio about a new type of banana that slices itself as it grows. Explain that these bananas are grown especially to be used in fruit salads. If the victim believes you, they may go and tell other people about this amazing new type of banana.

Practical 16

A Little Extra

One of the best things about A Little Extra is that there can be a number of victims.

The Sting

The whole family is sitting down for their evening meal. It's their favorite, spaghetti. The bowl of spaghetti is handed around and everyone serves themselves. Then the sauce is handed around and everyone scoops some out and pours it on top of their spaghetti. It smells so good. After the cheese is added, they tuck into their meal. The first person to swallow a mouthful screams and runs to the water tap. Suddenly, a second person follows. Then a third and a fourth. The sauce has been tampered with and is so spicy that no one can eat it.

What You Need: a hot, spicy food additive; a water supply where the meal is served

The Set-up

1 Get hold of a hot, spicy food additive. There may be some in your kitchen cupboard. Otherwise, you'll have to buy the additive from the store. Below are a few examples of the type of additive you can use:

- curry powder
- paprika
- chili pepper
- pepper
- tabasco sauce

2 Take out the additive when someone is cooking a spaghetti sauce or a stew or casserole. These are ideal meals to add an additive to because the additive will usually blend in and not be noticed until it is tasted.

3 When the cook leaves the kitchen, sneak in and pour your additive into the food. Stir it very well, then leave the cooking implements exactly as they were when the cook left the kitchen.

4 When the dinner is served and the victims start reaching for water, do the same. That way you won't be suspected of having played the joke.

This much CHILI PEPPER in the spaghetti sauce will guarantee takeout burgers for dinner tonight.

Set-up Tips

- Never play this joke if one of the possible victims is allergic to the food additive you are going to add. You do not want to make someone sick.
- The best day to play this joke is when you feel like takeout food. When the joke takes effect, it will be too late to cook another meal, so the whole family will have to get takeout.
- Many cooks taste their creations as they are cooking. If this is the case with your cook, then you are going to have to add the hot, spicy additive just before the meal is served.

This joke almost always works. It is quick and easy and makes the victim kick themselves for being made a fool of so easily.

The Sting

You tell the victim that they won't be able to give incorrect answers to four questions. Of course, the victim claims that they can easily give four incorrect answers. How easy it seems to them. They give an incorrect answer to the first question. Then they give an incorrect answer to the second question. Then they give an incorrect answer to the third question. One question to go and they are feeling very confident indeed. You throw in a comment that requires them to answer. They give a correct answer without realizing that this is the fourth question.

You're not catching me on this one...

Is this the 98th question or the 99th...? Or do you treat that as a question?

Smarty pants!

What You Need: nothing, except a victim

The Set-up

1 Tell your victim that you bet they can't give an incorrect answer to four questions you're going to ask them. They'll probably be so confident that you can bet them some money or get them to be your servant for a day if they fail the task.

Do I look like your dear old Granny?

It's a trick question. So I'll have to say Yes... Even though my Grandma would not be happy to hear me say that!

2 Make the first question an easy one. Something like 'Are you a boy?'. To give the incorrect answer, boys would answer 'No' and girls would answer 'Yes'. If they give the correct answer, then you've won your bet already.

3 Make the second question another easy one or even a silly one. Something like 'Am I your grandparent?'. They should answer 'Yes', as this is the incorrect answer. If they answer 'No', you've won.

4 The third question can also be easy. Ask them what day of the week it is. If they answer with today's day, you've won. If they answer with the wrong day, they're still in the contest. They're probably also feeling very confident.

5 Now, instead of asking the fourth question like the previous ones, say 'That's three questions I've asked now, isn't it?'. They will not expect that this is the fourth question and will answer 'Yes'. You then tell them that they have answered the fourth question correctly and have therefore lost the bet.

Computer Jokes

The Fast Mouse

Speedy Gonzales and Stuart Little have nothing on this mouse. This one moves so quickly, your victim won't even have time to blink.

The Sting

The victim of this joke sits down at their computer to surf the Internet or do some homework. They go to use their mouse. The cursor starts whizzing around the screen at twice the normal speed or is so slow the victim gets very frustrated.

What You Need: the victim's computer; two minutes alone with the computer

The Set-up

1 Make sure the victim is distracted for a couple of minutes. Perhaps arrange for one of your friends to call the victim at a particular time, when both you and your victim are at the victim's house.

2 Click the Start button on the computer taskbar.

3 Move the cursor to the Settings tag.

4 Click on Control Panel. The Control Panel box should open up.

5 Click on the icon for the Mouse. (If there is no Mouse icon, then click on 'view all Control Panel options', then click on the Mouse icon.) The Mouse Properties box should open up.

6 There should be a tag that reads Motion or Pointer Options. Press on this tag. It allows you to alter the speed of the mouse. Make the changes that you want, then press Apply.

7 Close all the boxes so that the computer looks exactly the way it did before you touched it.

Similar Jokes
There are other alterations you can make to the mouse. You can change the size and shape of the pointer, as well as the designs that appear when certain mouse functions take place. You can also change the functions of the buttons on the mouse and the clicking speed of the buttons.

New Screensaver

Practical

19

Here's an opportunity to make your mark on someone else's computer, without doing any lasting damage. If your victim's confused enough, they may even think their entire computer has been replaced.

The Sting

The victim of this joke leaves their computer for a few minutes to get something to eat, answer the phone, or for another reason. When they return, their normal screensaver has disappeared and been replaced by one that has a message saying 'You have been stung by [Your Name]' or 'I have gobbled up your screensaver', or by a humorous image.

What You Need; the victim's computer; three minutes alone with the computer

The Set-up

1 Make sure the victim is distracted for at least three minutes. Perhaps arrange for one of your friends to call the victim at a particular time, when both you and your victim are at the victim's house.

2 Click the Start button on the computer taskbar.

3 Move the cursor to the Settings tag.

4 Click on Control Panel. The Control Panel box should open up.

5 Click on the icon that reads Display. The Display Properties box should open up.

6 There should be a tag that reads Screen Saver. Press on this tag. It allows you to change the screensaver.

7 There is a box that contains a list of all the possible screensavers. Press on the arrow to the left of this box to bring up the choices. Select one, then press Apply.

8 If you choose Scrolling Marquee, then Settings, a box comes up allowing you to type in a message. This message will scroll across the screen when the screensaver is activated.

Similar Joke
You can also change the amount of time it takes for the screensaver to appear. Why not change the time to one minute, so that if the computer is idle for this short period, the screensaver will pop up. The victim will start getting very annoyed indeed.

New Wallpaper

Changing wallpaper usually involves hours of stripping, plastering, and gluing. With this trick, you can change the wallpaper in minutes, with no mess at all.

The Sting

The victim of this joke leaves their computer for a few minutes to get something to eat, answer the phone, or for another reason. When they return, their normal background, also known as wallpaper, has disappeared and been replaced by one with a humorous image.

What You Need: the victim's computer; three minutes alone with the computer

The Set-up

1 Make sure the victim is distracted for at least three minutes. Perhaps arrange for one of your friends to call the victim at a particular time, when both you and your victim are at the victim's house.

2 Click the Start button on the computer taskbar.

3 Move the cursor to the Settings tag.

4 Click on Control Panel. The Control Panel box should open up.

5 Click on the icon that reads Display. The Display Properties box should open up.

6 There should be a tag that reads Background. Press on this tag. It allows you to change the computer's background image.

7 There is a box that contains a list of all the possible background images. Select one, then press Apply.

8 Close all the boxes so that the computer looks exactly the way it did before you touched it.

Similar Joke
You can also change the way an image appears on the screen by clicking on Center, Tile or Stretch in the Background box.

This joke can be played on someone answering the phone or to an answering machine.

The Sting

The victim gets a phone call from someone asking for Joe Bloggs (or any other name). The victim explains that the caller must have the wrong number because Joe Bloggs does not live there. Not long after, another caller phones and asks for Joe Bloggs. This continues a number of times. The victim is getting more and more heated up. Finally, someone phones up and says, 'Hi, it's Joe Bloggs here. Have you got any messages for me?'.

What You Need: the telephone number of your victim; a number of people who can pose as callers without being recognized by the victim

The Set-up

1 Call up the victim and ask to speak to Joe Bloggs (or any name other than the victim's).

2 An hour later, get a second person to call up and ask to speak to Joe Bloggs.

3 An hour later, get a third person to call up and ask to speak to Joe Bloggs.

4 An hour later, get a fourth person to call up and ask to speak to Joe Bloggs.

5 When you have had as many different people as possible call up, make another call. This time, say, 'Hi, it's Joe Bloggs here. Have you got any messages for me?'.

Follow-up

If you know the victim's address as well as their phone number, you could send a few letters to Joe Bloggs, after you have finished with the telephone joke. Then ring the victim up a few days later and claim to be Joe Bloggs again. Ask the victim if they have any mail for you.

Set-up Tips

This joke can be over in a couple of hours or it can drag on for weeks. You can have your callers phone the victim one after the other, before you phone up claiming to be Joe Bloggs. Or you can arrange it so that the victim receives a call every day or two for a few weeks, before you call up claiming to be Joe Bloggs.

• Try to get your callers to each say something different, rather than all phoning and asking 'Is Joe Bloggs there?'. For example, one could be a telemarketer trying to sell something to Joe Bloggs. Another could be Joe's mother trying to get hold of him. Yet another could be a debt collector chasing Joe because he owes them money. The more variety, the better the joke.

• Of course, if the victim turns out to have the same name as the person you are leaving messages for, then you're going to have to do some pretty quick thinking.

Telephone Jokes

The Contest Winner

This joke involves leaving a message on an answering machine. It does not work if someone answers the phone.

The Sting

The victim gets home and sees they have a message on their answering machine. They press the 'Play' button and hear a message that says, 'This is a message for Pete [insert victim's name instead]. We are calling because you have won a great prize. It includes a holiday, spending money, a brand new mountain bike, and a big-screen TV. To claim your prize, all you have to do is ring 386 5 "beep beep beep".' The victim jumps up and down because it appears as if the answering machine has cut out before the person has given the full telephone number.

What You Need: the telephone number of your victim; a victim with an answering machine; a tape recorder

---

The Set-up

1 Make sure there is no one at the victim's house.

2 Telephone the victim.

3 When the answering machine kicks in, leave a message pretending you are calling from a radio station to tell the victim they have won a fantastic prize. All the victim has to do is call a particular phone number by the end of the day.

4 Start giving out a phone number. When you have got three numbers left, hang up suddenly.

Set-up Tips

• When making the call, disguise your voice or get someone the victim doesn't know to leave the message.
• Write down exactly what you are going to say, then read it out. This will make it sound more professional and less like you are making things up as you go along.
• The 'beep beep beep' sound that appears at the end is not really coming from their answering machine but is a sound you make. You could say it yourself and make it sound like a machine, or you could tape the sound of your own answering machine beeping, then play the sound back.

Follow-up

You can extend the joke the next day by leaving a message that says, 'Hi Pete. We called yesterday about the great prize you've won. We'll give you another day to call us, then offer the prize to someone else. In case you've lost our phone number, it is 986 5 "beep beep beep".'

Wrong Numbers

This joke results in the victim phoning lots of wrong numbers. It's great fun listening to the confusion that you have caused. This will only work on phones with automatic dial buttons.

The Sting

Your victim wants to phone someone they talk with regularly. They talk to this person so often that they have them on automatic dial. That means the victim has programmed their phone to automatically dial a particular number when a particular button is pressed. The victim presses the button that they always press. But they get through to someone else. They try again but the same thing happens. When they try another automatic dial number, they get another wrong number. They soon discover that all of their automatic dial numbers have been changed.

What You Need; a victim with a telephone with automatic dial buttons; about ten minutes to carry out the joke

The Set-up

1 Make sure the victim's phone has automatic dial buttons that they have programmed. The best indication that someone uses the automatic dial function on their phone is a sticker with someone's name under or next to each button.

2 You then have to work out how to change the numbers. See if you can find the instruction booklet for the phone. It will contain the instructions that you need.

3 You can put in completely new numbers at random or the phone numbers of people you know.

4 If you know the phone numbers for all the people listed on the automatic dial buttons, you could swap these phone numbers around. That will really confuse the victim.

5 If you don't know how to change the numbers, just swap the stickers around. This will confuse the victim for a short time.

Set-up Tips
• Never change the number for an emergency service, such as a doctor or the local police station. People only phone these numbers in emergencies and you don't want your joke to cause distress.
• Don't replace one of the automatic dial numbers with that of an emergency service. Emergency services are busy enough without having to deal with wrong numbers.

Practical

24

A New Outfit

The time to play this joke is when you've spotted a great shirt, pair of pants or skirt in a store. You can't afford to buy it yourself and you doubt your parents will buy it for you. But if this joke is successful, the chances are you're going to have that new piece of clothing the same day.

The Sting

Your mother or father starts pulling wet clothes out of the washing machine. Suddenly they stop in shock. They pull out an item of your clothing that is ripped to shreds. It must have got caught up in one of the washing machine parts. When they show it to you, you get very upset. You may even burst into tears. You tell them it was your favorite item of clothing and that nothing could replace it. Then you suddenly remember that there is one item of clothing that could possibly replace it.

> **What You Need: an old item of clothing; a pair of scissors; a washing machine**

The Set-up

1 A few days before you play this joke, wear an old item of clothing and mention to your parents how much you like it. In reality, you should choose something you are not very keen on at all.

2 Wear the item of clothing at least once more over the next day or so.

3 When you're ready to play the joke, grab a pair of scissors and make a few small cuts in the piece of clothing.

4 Make the cuts larger by ripping them with your hands. This helps disguise the neat cuts made by the scissors.

5 Wait until one of your parents has put a load of laundry into the washing machine. When they have turned the machine on and walked away, sneak in and put your item of clothing into the machine.

6 When your parent shows you the torn clothing, get very upset. Try and put on an Academy Award-winning acting performance.

7 When your parent tries to cheer you up, mention the item of clothing that you saw in the shop. However, do not mention it too early or they may get suspicious.

Yesterday's News

Sometimes today's news seems very similar to yesterday's news. With this joke, today's news is *exactly the same* as yesterday's news.

> Where do they get today's news? From yesterday's paper? The largest ocean liner in the world has just been launched AGAIN for the first time... today!

> And the first lady to swim around the world yesterday... has just swum around it again... today for the first time!

The Sting

Your mother or father sits down to read the newspaper over breakfast. As they eat their cereal and drink their coffee, they read the front page. Then they read the second page. So far, they're reading the latest news. They go onto the third page, then the fourth page, and so on. The further they get into the newspaper, the more they begin to feel as if they've read it all before. They check the date on the front page, but it's certainly today's newspaper. So they go back to reading. Finally, they come across a story that they are sure they've read before. They check the date on that page. It's yesterday's date. Somehow, the inside pages of the newspaper are from the day before.

What You Need: an old newspaper (preferably from the day before); today's newspaper

The Set-up

1 The day before you are going to play the joke, keep the newspaper after it has been read.

2 If you get the newspaper delivered to your house, get up nice and early on the day that you are going to play the joke so that you are the first to get to the paper.

3 If someone in your house usually goes to the store to buy the newspaper, on the day that you are going to play the joke, offer to go and buy it.

4 Take all of the inside pages out of today's newspaper. You should be left with the front and back pages, as well as the second and second last pages.

5 Take the inside pages out of yesterday's newspaper and place them inside the front and back pages of today's newspaper.

6 Put the newspaper in its usual place.

7 Sit near your parent as they read the newspaper. See how long it takes them to notice that they're reading yesterday's news.

> Here Dad! I've just been to the store to get you the latest up to the minute news from around the world!

> I'm sure you'll find it just as interesting as yesterday's news!

Practical 26

Tool Box

If your dad loves fixing things around the house, you can give him a big surprise by playing the Tool Box practical joke.

The Sting

The victim decides it's time they fix that broken chair that has been stored in the corner of the shed for months, ever since it fell apart when your great aunt sat on it. The victim goes into the shed, grabs their tool box, and puts the chair on top of the workbench. The first thing they need to do is unscrew the chair legs. They open their tool box and reach for their screwdriver. They find a screwdriver but it's not the one they usually use. It's a plastic screwdriver. Their hammer is also plastic. In fact, every one of their tools has been replaced by a toy tool. The victim looks at the wall of their shed where their saws usually hang. These too have been replaced by plastic saws. Even their power drill is a toy drill.

What You Need; the victim's tool box; plastic tools

The Set-up

1 Buy or borrow lots of toy tools.

2 Find out where your victim keeps their tools.

3 When your victim is not around, replace their tools with the toy tools. (Be very careful handling the real tools. Some tools have very sharp edges and points. To be extra safe, wear thick gloves.)

4 Hide the real tools.

5 If your victim shows no sign of wanting to use their tool box, point out that something around the house needs fixing.

Similar Joke
Rather than replacing the real tools with toy tools, you could hide the real tools around the house, shed, and garden, and leave notes in the tool box that offer clues to where the tools can be found.

Whoopee

Whoopee cushions are one of the most popular items in practical joke shops. One whoopee cushion can cause embarrassment to many, many people. Try a whoopee cushion next time your parents have visitors over.

The Sting

Some of your parents' friends have come over for dinner. They are standing around talking before dinner is served. One of them decides to sit down on the sofa. They walk over and take a seat. The moment their bottom hits the cushion, a loud sound breaks out. It sounds like someone breaking wind. Everybody turns to look at the victim who has turned red with embarrassment.

What You Need: a whoopee cushion; a sofa or chair with cushions

The Set-up

1. Buy a whoopee cushion from a joke or magic shop.

2. Blow some air into the cushion. You do not need to blow the cushion all the way up. If it is too full, you may not be able to hide it under a sofa cushion.

3. Just before your parents' friends come over, place the cushion under a sofa cushion.

4. Hide where you can see the sofa but where you cannot be seen.

5. Wait for the fun to begin.

Similar Joke

You don't have to place the whoopee cushion on a chair or sofa to make the joke work. Try hiding under the dinner table and place the whoopee cushion under your arm. As each person sits down, press your arm down so that the whoopee cushion makes its noise. The only problem is escaping from under the table without being seen.

The Stirrer

Practical 28

You can play this joke whenever one of your parents' friends pops in for a cup of tea or coffee. But don't play it on the same person twice or they'll get suspicious.

The Sting

The victim accepts your offer of a cup of coffee. You bring them their cup and teaspoon, as well as the milk and sugar. The victim adds a bit of milk to the coffee, then takes the teaspoon and spoons some sugar into the cup. They then stir their coffee. When they take the teaspoon out, they're left with only the handle—the bottom part has fallen off. They have no idea how it happened, but they feel very embarrassed.

What You Need: an old teaspoon; some chewing gum; a hot cup of tea or coffee

The Set-up

1 Buy an old teaspoon from a second-hand shop or use an old one from home. Make sure you don't use a valuable teaspoon or someone's favorite spoon because you are going to destroy it.

2 Grab the oval end of the teaspoon with one hand and hold the handle tightly with the other hand.

3 Wiggle the oval end until you feel it loosening. It will eventually break off.

4 When it has broken off, get a tiny piece of chewing gum and stick the two pieces back together. Make sure that the gum cannot be seen. You only need enough to stop the spoon breaking when it is picked up.

5 Give the victim the spoon with their hot drink. It has to be a hot drink because the heat will melt the gum.

6 As the victim stirs sugar or milk into their drink, tell them that the spoon is your favorite because it was given to you by a very special friend. This will make them feel even worse when it breaks.

Similar Joke

You can play this joke on a whole bunch of people at once. If you know that your parents are going to host a dinner party, prepare several spoons in the way described above and make sure that they are set out on the table with the coffee and tea.

Short Sheet

Practical 29

This joke will irritate your brother and sister just when they least want to be irritated—when they're getting into bed. It's a very common joke and an easy one to play, but it only works on beds with top sheets.

The Sting

The victim is ready for bed. They are in their pajamas, have cleaned their teeth and have said goodnight to everyone. They turn down the covers on their bed and put their feet under the sheet. The only problem is they can't push their feet down to the bottom of the bed. No matter how hard they push, the sheet won't let them stretch out. They may have been relaxed when they started to get into bed but now they're hopping mad.

What You Need: five minutes alone in your victim's bedroom

The Set-up

1 Take the top sheet and the blanket or duvet off the bed.

2 Hide the top sheet. You don't need it any more.

3 Undo the bottom sheet from the bottom end of the bed.

4 Fold the sheet in half, so that both the ends are at the top end of the bed.

5 Put the blanket or duvet back on the bed, then fold the top part of the sheet over the top of the blanket or duvet.

6 The sheet should now only go halfway down the bed but, from the outside, everything appears normal.

7 Wait to hear the shouts from the victim.

Special Note
Of course, this joke won't work if your brother or sister never makes their bed. They'll suspect something immediately if they see a neat bed.

Practical

30

Wakey, Wakey

Don't play this joke on a brother or sister if you share a bedroom with them. Otherwise, the joke will be on you as well.

The Sting

It's four o'clock in the morning and your brother or sister is sound asleep. They had a late night and they went to bed looking forward to sleeping in. At four o'clock, their alarm clock goes off. It wakes them up. They're so sleepy that they try and think why they set the alarm to go off at four o'clock. They can't think of any reason so they just turn the alarm clock off and go back to sleep. They never do find out why their alarm clock went off.

This time of the morning... it's going to take her ten minutes just to turn the alarm off

What You Need; an alarm clock; a tired brother or sister; a flash light (for Follow-up)

Tell me you didn't set my alarm clock for 4.00am

OK..I didn't set your alarm clock for 4.00am !

The Set-up

1 Before your brother or sister goes to bed, sneak into their room. (The best time to do this is when they are out with friends, watching their favorite TV show, or having a bath or shower. This way it's unlikely you'll be seen.)

2 Set your brother's or sister's alarm clock to go off very early.

Follow-up

• If your brother or sister asks whether you played a joke on them, say 'No'. If you admit to playing the joke, they may try to get back at you.

• If you think that your brother or sister suspects you, make sure that you check your alarm clock before you go to sleep. They may try to play the same trick on you.

• If you are willing to get up early, you can continue the joke. Set your alarm to go off at the same time as your brother's or sister's alarm. Allow your brother or sister about fifteen minutes to get back to sleep, then sneak into their room. You may need a flash light to see what you're doing. Set their alarm to go off again in an hour's time. Repeat this throughout the morning for as long as you think you can get away with it.

Change the Channel

Practical

31

Some brothers and sisters spend a lot of time arguing about which TV program they're going to watch. When this happens, the remote control is a very important weapon.

The Sting

You are watching a TV program when your brother or sister joins you. They do not like the program you are watching and start complaining about it. You tell them to be quiet and let you watch the program in peace. They reach for the remote control and press the button for the channel they want to watch. Nothing happens. They press the button a bit harder. Still nothing happens. They start pressing all the buttons, one after the other. Still nothing happens. You laugh to yourself as you happily watch your favorite TV program to the very end. Your victim gets so frustrated that they storm off to their room, leaving you to watch whatever you like for the whole night.

What You Need: a TV remote control; a TV set

The Set-up

1 Set the TV to the channel you want to watch.

2 Take the batteries out of the remote control.

3 Hide the batteries.

4 Hide any other batteries that fit the remote control.

5 Put the remote control in its usual place, then sit back and wait for the fun to start.

Similar Jokes

If you really want to drive someone crazy, reprogram the remote control so that the buttons no longer relate to the right channels. To do this, you'll need half an hour alone with the remote control. If there's one particular channel that you know the victim does not like, reprogram every button so that they all control that channel.

Transport Jokes

Practical

All in Order

It is amazing that this joke works because it seems so silly. However, you'll be surprised how easily people are fooled.

The Sting

The victim skates towards you on their skateboard. You yell something and gesture towards the back of their skateboard. They stop and check their skateboard, before realizing they've been the butt of a joke. After all, you didn't say that anything was wrong.

> **What You Need; nothing, just a victim with a skateboard**

The Set-up

1 As the victim skateboards towards you, gesture towards the back of their skateboard and yell out, 'Your back wheels are going round'.

2 You haven't told the victim that something is wrong. In fact you're telling them that everything is OK. However, the way that you gesture and the tone of your voice suggests that there is a problem.

3 Stand back and watch the victim as they get off their skateboard and check that everything is OK. When they realize that there is no problem, they'll probably think back and remember what you said. Then they'll realize they've been the victim of a practical joke.

Similar Jokes
- For people cycling past on a bicycle, you can call out, 'Your back wheel is going around' or 'Your pedals are turning'.
- For joggers or walkers going past, you can point to their shoes and call out, 'Your shoelaces are done up'.
- For people driving cars or riding motorbikes, you can call out, 'You've got exhaust coming out of the back' or 'Your engine is working'.

Parking Ticket is a joke to play on people with cars. It is particularly amusing if you can be near the victim when they find what they think is a parking ticket.

The Sting

The victim parks their car in a two-hour parking spot. They go off to do some shopping and return after an hour. They put the shopping into the trunk of their car and walk around to the front. They stop in horror when they see a parking ticket on their windshield. They check the words on the parking sign, then check their watch. They can't understand how they got a ticket. By now, they are pretty angry. They rip the ticket off their windshield and open it up to see how much they have been fined. The ticket reads 'Thank you for parking legally. Have a nice day'.

What You Need: colored paper; sticky tape; a sheet of plastic; a parking ticket

The Set-up

1 Have a look at a parking ticket. If someone in your family gets one, ask to have a look. If you can't get hold of a parking ticket, walk down the street and see if you can spot a car with a parking ticket. Don't touch it, but notice what color it is, what size it is, and how it is folded and taped to the windshield.

2 Buy some paper the same color as the parking ticket. Cut it to size and write a message on it. The message should let the driver know they have been the victim of a practical joke.

3 Fold the paper to the right size.

4 You may want to wrap the ticket in plastic before taping it to a windshield.

5 Go to a busy street where there are parking restrictions and put the ticket on the windshield of a parked car. Make sure the driver does not see you.

6 Wait nearby and watch the reaction of the victim when they return to their car. Most people are pretty angry when they get a parking ticket, especially when they know they have done nothing wrong.

7 Watch if their reaction changes when they read the message you wrote.

Practical

34

Fly Away

The creatures in this joke aren't real, but the victim certainly thinks they are.

The Sting

The victim decides to make a sandwich. They get out the bread, butter, and jam. When they open the butter container, they see a fly sitting on the butter. They decide to do without butter and just have the jam. But when they open the jam jar, there is a fly in there as well. Yuk! They check the sugar bowl. A fly is in there. There's also a fly in the fruit bowl and another on the kitchen counter. Thinking that there must be a fly plague, they run to the store to get some fly spray.

What You Need: plastic flies; enough time to plant the flies in the victim's kitchen

The Set-up

1 Buy some plastic flies. You can get them at a joke or magic shop. (Never use dead flies for this joke because even dead flies carry lots of germs. You don't want to make anyone sick.)

2 When the victim is out of their kitchen, sneak in and put the flies in different places. It's best to place them on food items because the victim will feel ill when they find them.

3 Place several flies in the sugar bowl. Every time the victim reaches for the sugar over the next few weeks, they won't be able to get the image of the flies out of their mind.

4 Hide somewhere near the kitchen so that you can see or hear the victim's reaction.

Follow-up

If you want to really turn your victim's stomach, walk into the kitchen soon after they have discovered the flies. Tell the victim that you heard on the radio that flies are very nutritious. Then grab one and pop it in your mouth. Pretend to chew it, but make sure you don't really swallow the plastic fly.

COOL JOKES

COOL JOKES

Whether it's kooky knock-knock jokes, silly sports jokes, or even just a quick quip, people love to laugh. In fact, babies laugh before they learn to speak, and scientists say even some animals can make laughing sounds when they are happy.

Lucky for you, we created this section with hundreds of fantastically funny jokes to keep you, your friends, and even your pets laughing all day long!

Contents

1 What do you get when you cross an elephant with a fish?
Swimming trunks!

2 What do you get when an elephant sits on your friend?
A flat mate.

3 How did the skunk phone his mother?
On a smellular phone.

4 Why are four-legged animals bad dancers?
Because they have two left feet.

5 What do you call a lamb with a machine gun?
Lambo.

6 What's fifty meters long and jumps every ten seconds?
A dinosaur with the hiccups.

7 What do you get when you cross a mountain lion and a parrot?
I don't know, but when it talks, you had better listen!

8 What do you get when you cross a chicken and a caterpillar?
Drumsticks for everyone!

9 What do you call a camel with three humps?
Humphrey.

10 What do you get if you sit under a cow?
A pat on the head.

11 What kind of tie do pigs wear?
A pigsty.

12 Which side of the chicken has the most feathers?
The outside.

13 What did the duck say when she finished shopping?
Just put it on my bill.

14 What did the hen say when she saw scrambled eggs?
What a crazy mixed up kid.

15 Why do mother kangaroos hate rainy days?
Because their kids have to play inside.

16 What do you call an elephant in a telephone box?
Stuck.

17 What do you call an elephant that never washes?
A smellyphant.

18 Why do elephants live in the jungle?
Because they can't fit inside houses.

19 Which bird can never be trusted?
A lyre-bird.

20 What do you get if you cross a parrot with a shark?
An animal that talks your head off!

21 What's black and white and eats like a horse?
A zebra.

22 What do you get if you cross a centipede with a parrot?
A walkie-talkie.

23 What did the snail say when he hitched a ride on the turtle's back?
Weeeeeeeeeeeeeeeeeeeeeee!!!!

24 What's black and white and black and white and black and white?
A penguin rolling down a hill!

25 What is white, fluffy and lives in the jungle?
A meringue-utan!

26 What's bright orange and sounds like a parrot?
A carrot!

27 What is a slug?
A snail with a housing problem.

28 What's the difference between an elephant and a flea?
An elephant can have fleas but a flea can't have elephants.

29 What steps would you take if a bull chased you?
Big ones.

30 What happened to the dog that swallowed the watch?
He got ticks.

31 Why is the sky so high?
So birds won't bump their heads.

32 Why do giraffes have long necks?
Because their feet stink.

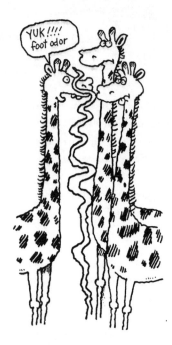

33 Where do bees go when they're sick?
To the waspital!

34 What swings through the trees and is very dangerous?
A chimpanzee with a machine-gun.

35 What time is it when an elephant sits on your fence?
Time to get a new fence.

36 What do you call a baby whale?
A little squirt.

37 What are feathers good for?
Birds.

38 Are you a vegetarian because you love animals?
No, because I don't like plants.

39 Why did they cross a homing pigeon with a parrot?
So if it got lost it could ask for directions.

40 What has four legs and goes 'Boo'?
A cow with a cold.

41 Ten cats were on a boat, one jumped off, how many were left?
None, they were all copycats!

42 What's black and white and makes a terrible noise?
A penguin playing the bagpipes.

43 What do you get when you cross an elephant with a sparrow?
Broken telephone poles everywhere.

44 Who went into the tiger's lair and came out alive?
The tiger.

45 How do you start a flea race?
One, two, flea, go!

46 What do frogs order in restaurants?
French flies!

47 Why does a hummingbird hum?
It doesn't know the words!

48 Did you put the cat out?
I didn't know it was on fire!

49 How do you know that carrots are good for your eyesight?
Have you ever seen a rabbit wearing glasses?

50 What does a crab use to call someone?
A shellular phone!

51 What has four legs and sees just as well from both ends?
A horse with his eyes closed.

52 What do you get when you cross a cat with a lemon?
A sour puss!

53 What kind of cat shouldn't you play cards with?
A cheetah!

54 Hickory dickory dock,
Three mice ran up the clock,
The clock struck one,
But the other two got away with minor injuries.

55 What do you give a dog with a fever?
Mustard, it's the best thing for a hot dog!

56 Why do cows wear bells?
Because their horns don't work!

57 What did the porcupine say to the cactus?
Are you my mother?

58 What happened to the snake with a cold?
She adder viper nose.

59 What's the difference between a unicorn and a lettuce?
One is a funny beast and the other a bunny feast.

60 What did Tarzan say when he saw the elephants coming over the hill?
Here come the elephants over the hill.

61 Where do you put a noisy dog?
In a barking lot!

62 What did the caterpillar say to the butterfly?
You'll never get me up in one of those things.

63 What do you call a fly when it retires?
A flew.

64 What do you get when you cross an elephant with peanut butter?
Either an elephant that sticks to the roof of your mouth or peanut butter that never forgets.

65 What game do elephants play in a Volkswagen?
Squash!

66 Why do tigers eat raw meat?
Because they can't cook.

67 Now you see it, now you don't, now you see it, now you don't. What is it?
A black cat on a crosswalk.

68 What do you call an unmarried female moth?
Myth.

69 What do you get if you cross an alligator with a camera?
A snapshot.

70 What do you get from nervous cows?
Milk shakes.

71 Why do elephants' tusks stick out?
Because their parents can't afford braces!

72 What's the biggest mouse in the world?
A hippopotamouse.

73 Why didn't the piglets listen to their father?
Because he was a boar.

74 Why did the lion spit out the clown?
Because he tasted funny.

75 What did the beaver say to the tree?
It's been nice gnawing you.

76 How do you make toast in the jungle?
Put your bread under a gorilla.

77 How do you tell which end of a worm is the head?
Tickle him in the middle and watch where he smiles.

78 How do you stop an elephant from smelling?
Tie a knot in his trunk.

79 What should you know if you want to be a lion tamer?
More than the lion.

80 Why did the fly fly?
Because the spider spied her.

81 Why don't kangaroos ride bicycles?
Because they don't have thumbs to ring the little bell.

82 What's the same size and shape as an elephant but weighs nothing?
An elephant's shadow.

83 How do you get an elephant up an acorn tree?
Sit him on an acorn and wait twenty years.

84 What did one flea say to the other?
Shall we walk or take the dog?

85 What goes tick tick woof?
A watch dog.

86 Why was the chicken sick?
Because it had people pox.

87 What do elephants have that no other animal does?
Baby elephants.

88 What's big, white, furry, and found in outback Australia?
A very lost polar bear.

89 Why do horses only wear shoes?
Because they would look silly with socks on.

90 What's the difference between an African elephant and an Indian elephant?
About 6000 kilometres.

91 What do you get if you cross a dinosaur with a vampire?
A blood shortage.

92 What do dinosaurs put on their chips?
Tomatosaurus.

93 What do you call a blind dinosaur?
Do-ya-think-he-saw-us?

94 What do you call a dinosaur that's a noisy sleeper?
Brontosnorus.

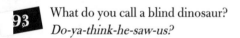

95 What do dinosaurs put on their floors?
Rep-tiles.

96 Why couldn't the long-necked dinosaur see?
Because it had its head in the clouds!

97 What do you call a one-hundred million year old dinosaur?
A fossil.

98 Why didn't the dinosaur cross the road?
Because roads weren't invented.

99 What do you call a dinosaur that destroys everything in its path?
Tyrannosaurus Wrecks.

100 What do you call a scared tyrannosaurus?
A nervous rex.

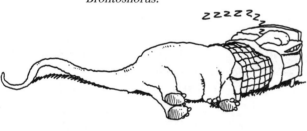

101 Why is six scared of seven?
Because 7-8-9.

102 What did the egg say to the whisk?
I know when I'm beaten.

103 Why did the toilet paper roll down the hill?
To get to the bottom.

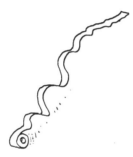

104 Where are the Andes?
At the end of your armies.

105 What helps keep your teeth together?
Toothpaste.

106 What do you call a ship that lies on the bottom of the ocean and shakes?
A nervous wreck!

107 How do you make a hotdog stand?
Steal its chair!

108 What's the best way to win a race?
Run faster than everyone else.

109 Can a match box?
No but a tin can.

110 During which battle was Lord Nelson killed?
His last one.

111 What did the floor say to the desk?
I can see your drawers.

112 Why did the surfer stop surfing?
Because the sea weed.

113 What was more useful than the invention of the first telephone?
The second telephone.

114 How do you use an Egyptian doorbell?
Toot-and-come-in.

115 What side of an apple is the left side?
The side that hasn't been eaten.

116 What invention allows you to see through walls?
A window.

117 How did the dentist become a brain surgeon?
His drill slipped.

118 Which months have 28 days?
All of them.

119 Where does Tarzan buy his clothes?
At a jungle sale.

120 How do you make a fire with two sticks?
Make sure one of them is a match.

121 Why does lightning shock people?
It doesn't know how to conduct itself.

122 What did the pencil sharpener say to the pencil?
Stop going in circles and get to the point!

123 What do Alexander the Great and Kermit the Frog have in common?
The same middle name!

124 What's the easiest way to get on TV?
Sit on it.

125 What has four legs and doesn't walk?
A table.

126 Name three inventions that have helped man up in the world.
The elevator, the ladder, and the alarm clock.

127 What's easy to get into but hard to get out of?
Trouble.

128 Mom, why isn't my nose twelve inches long?
Because then it would be a foot.

129 What has many rings but no fingers?
A telephone.

130 What do you get if you jump into the Red Sea?
Wet.

131 What's brown and sticky?
A stick.

Miscellaneous Jokes

132 How do you make holy water?
You burn the hell out of it.

133 What do you get if you cross the Atlantic with the Titanic?
About half way.

134 Why did the bacteria cross the microscope?
To get to the other slide.

135 What's the hardest part about sky diving?
The ground!

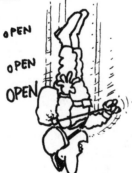

136 Why did the traffic light turn red?
You would too if you had to change in the middle of the street!

137 How much does it cost for a pirate to get earrings?
A buccaneer!

138 What did the digital clock say to its mother?
Look Ma, no hands.

139 What did one rain drop say to the other?
Two's company, three's a cloud.

140 What do hippies do?
They hold your leggies on.

141 What do you call a snowman with a suntan?
A puddle!

142 What did the Pacific Ocean say to the Atlantic Ocean?
Nothing. It just waved.

143 What can jump higher than a house?
Anything, houses can't jump!

144 What sort of star is dangerous?
A shooting star.

145 Why did the belt go to jail?
Because it held up a pair of pants.

146 What's the difference between an elephant and a matterbaby?
What's a matterbaby?
Nothing, but thanks for asking!

147 What did the shirt say to the blue jeans?
Meet you on the clothesline—that's where I hang out!

148 What did the big hand of the clock say to the little hand?
Got a minute?

149 What's the easiest way to find a pin in your carpet?
Walk around in your bare feet.

150 What's the definition of intense?
That's where campers sleep.

151 What do you call a man who stands around and makes faces all day?
A clockmaker.

152 What did one toilet say to the other toilet?
You look a bit flushed!

153 When does B come after U?
When you take some of its honey!

154 What's green, sits in the corner and cries?
The Incredible Sulk.

155 What do vampires cross the sea in?
Blood vessels.

156 What did King Kong say when his sister had a baby?
Well I'll be a monkey's uncle.

157 Why did the zombie decide to stay in his coffin?
He felt rotten.

158 What happened when the abominable snowman ate a curry?
He melted.

159 What do sea monsters eat for lunch?
Potato ships!

160 Why did the cyclops give up teaching?
Because he only had one pupil.

161 Why do witches fly on broomsticks?
Because it's better than walking.

162 Why did Dracula take some medicine?
To stop his coffin.

163 What do devils drink?
Demonade.

164 What don't zombies wear on boat trips?
Life jackets.

165 What do you call a sleeping monster who won't keep quiet?
Frankensnore

166 What happened to Frankenstein's monster when he was caught speeding?
He was fined $50 and dismantled for six months.

167 How does a monster count to thirteen?
On his fingers.

168 What happened to the monster that took the five o'clock train home?
He had to give it back.

169 What kind of cheese do monsters eat?
Monsterella!

170 What do you get when you cross a vampire and a snowman?
Frostbite!

171 What do you call a monster that was locked in the freezer overnight?
A cool ghoul!

172 What did the witch say to the vampire?
Get a life.

173 What do you get when you cross a skunk with Frankenstein?
Stinkenstein!

174 What is a vampire's favorite kind of coffee?
De-coffin-ated!

175 How can you tell a Martian would be a good gardener?
They all have green thumbs!

176 What does a monster say when introduced?
Pleased to eat you.

177 Why did the sea monster eat five ships carrying potatoes?
Because you can't just eat one potato ship.

178 Why doesn't anyone kiss vampires?
Because they have bat breath.

179 What do you think the tiniest vampire gets up to at night?
Your ankles.

180 Why do ghosts go to parties?
To have a wail of a time.

181 Why do ghosts hate rain?
It dampens their spirits.

182 Why did they call the Cyclops a playboy?
Because he had an eye for the ladies!

183 What did one ghost say to the other?
Don't spook until you're spooken to!

184 What do you call a witch that lives at the beach?
A sand witch!

185 How do you make a witch scratch?
Take away the W!

186 Why do mummies have trouble keeping friends?
They're too wrapped up in themselves.

187 How many witches does it take to change a light bulb?
Just one, but she changes it into a toad!

188 Who is the best dancer at a monster party?
The Boogie Man!

189 Where does a ghost go on Saturday nights?
Somewhere he can boogie!

190 Why did the one armed monster cross the road?
To get to the second hand shop.

 191 Why can't the Invisible Man pass school?
The teacher always marks him absent!

192 Why did the monster eat the North Pole?
He was in the mood for a frozen dinner!

193 What is the best way to call Frankenstein's monster?
Long distance!

194 What kind of mistake does a ghost make?
A boo-boo!

195 Why do they have a fence around the graveyard?
Everyone is dying to get in!

196 What did the vampire say when he had bitten someone?
It's been nice gnawing you!

197 What did the skeleton say to the twin witches?
Which witch is which?

198 Why is the vampire so unpopular?
Because he is a pain in the neck!

199 What does a ghost do when he gets in a car?
Puts his sheet belt on!

200 Why didn't the ghost eat liver?
He didn't have the stomach for it!

201 What kind of fur do you get from a werewolf?
As fur away as you can get!

202 Who did the monster take to the Halloween dance?
His ghoul friend!

203 What do you call a monster sleeping in a chandelier?
A light sleeper.

204 Why are ghosts such terrible liars?
Because you can see right through them.

205 What's a skeleton?
Someone with their outside off and their insides out.

206 What did one skeleton say to the other?
If we had any guts we'd get out of here!

207 What do you call a vampire's dog?
A blood hound!

208 How do you know when a ghost is sad?
He says 'Boooooooooo hooooooooo'!

209 Doctor, Doctor, I have a hoarse throat.
The resemblance doesn't end there.

210 Doctor, Doctor, I feel like a tennis racket.
You must be too highly strung.

211 Doctor, Doctor, I keep stealing things.
Take one of these pills and if that doesn't work, bring me back a computer.

212 Doctor, Doctor, I think I'm a video.
I thought I'd seen you before.

213 Doctor, Doctor, how can I stop my nose from running?
Stick your foot out and trip it up.

214 Doctor, Doctor, everyone hates me.
Don't be stupid, not everyone has met you yet.

215 Doctor, Doctor, I feel run down.
You should be more careful crossing the road then.

216 Doctor, Doctor, I'm at death's door.
Don't worry, I'll pull you through.

217 Doctor, Doctor, I feel like a dog!
Then go see a vet!

218 Doctor, Doctor, I keep thinking I'm a doorknob.
Now don't fly off the handle.

219 Doctor, Doctor, I feel like a cricket ball.
How's that?
Oh no, not you too!

220 Doctor, Doctor, I swallowed a spoon.
Well try to relax and don't stir.

221 Doctor, Doctor, I swallowed a roll of film.
Don't worry, nothing will develop.

222 Doctor, Doctor, nobody ever listens to me.
Next!

223 Doctor, Doctor, I'm turning into a trashcan.
Don't talk such rubbish.

224 Doctor, Doctor, I'm as sick as a dog.
Well I can't help you because I'm not a vet.

225 Doctor, Doctor, my eyesight is getting worse.
You're absolutely right, this is a Post Office.

226 Doctor, Doctor, I feel like a set of curtains.
Well pull yourself together.

227 Doctor, Doctor, I have a ringing in my ears!
Well answer it.

228 Doctor, Doctor, it hurts when I do this!
Well don't do that.

229 Why did the doctor tiptoe past the medicine cabinet?
Because she didn't want to wake the sleeping pills!

230 Doctor, Doctor, everyone thinks I'm a liar.
I don't believe you.

231 Doctor, Doctor, I have a pain in the eye every time I drink hot chocolate!
Take the spoon out of your mug before you drink.

232 Doctor, Doctor, I only have 59 seconds to live!
Just a minute!

233 Doctor, Doctor—I'm invisible!
I'm sorry, sir, I can't see you right now.

234 Doctor, Doctor, my hair is falling out. Can you give me something to keep it in?
Yes, a paper bag.

235 What did one tonsil say to the other tonsil?
Get dressed up, the doctor is taking us out!

236 Doctor, Doctor, what's good for biting fingernails?
Very sharp teeth.

237 How do you make a hankie dance?
Put some boogie into it.

238 What is the soft stuff between sharks' teeth?
Slow swimmers.

239 What's a sick joke?
Something that comes up in conversation.

240 What's the difference between a maggot and a cockroach?
Cockroaches crunch more when you eat them.

241 What do you get if you cross an elephant with a box of laxatives?
Out of the way.

242 What is the difference between broccoli and boogers?
Kids don't like to eat broccoli!

243 What's invisible and smells of carrots?
Bunny farts!!

244 What's the last thing that goes through a bug's mind when he hits a car windshield?
His bum.

245 How can you tell when a moth farts?
He flies straight for a second.

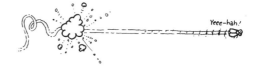

246 What's green and smells of eucalyptus?
Koala vomit.

247 How do you know when a fool has been making chocolate chip cookies?
There are M&M shells on the floor!

248 What's that on your shoulder?
A birthmark.
How long have you had it?

249 Why did the fool climb the glass wall?
To see what was on the other side!

250 Why did the fool get fired from the banana factory?
He threw out all the bent ones.

251 How many fools does it take to screw in a light bulb?
Three. One to hold the bulb, and two to turn the chair!

252 How do you confuse a fool?
Put him in a round room and tell him to sit in the corner!

253 How do you keep a fool in suspense?
I'll tell you tomorrow!

254 Why did the fool get fired from the M&M factory?
Because he threw away all the W's.

255 How do you get a one armed fool out of a tree?
Wave to him.

256 How can you tell when a fool has been using the computer?
There is whiteout all over the screen!

257 How did the fool break his arm while raking leaves?
He fell out of the tree!

258 Three fools were driving down the highway trying to get to Disneyland. They saw a sign that read 'Disneyland left.'
So they went home.

259 How do you make a fool laugh on a Sunday?
Tell him a joke on Saturday.

260 What did the farmer say when he lost his tractor?
'Where's my tractor?'

261 How did the fool fall on the floor?
He tripped over the cordless phone!

262 What did the fool say when he saw cheese rings?
Oh look, donut seeds!

263 How do you sink a submarine full of fools?
Knock on the door.

264 What happened to the fool tap dancer?
She fell in the sink.

265
Knock Knock
Who's there?
Cargo.
Cargo who?
Car go beep beep!

266
Knock Knock
Who's there?
Police.
Police who?
Police let me in.

267
Knock knock
Who's there?
Gotter.
Gotter who?
Gotter go to the toilet.

268
Knock Knock
Who's there?
Norma Lee.
Norma Lee who?
Norma Lee I'd be at school
but I've got the day off.

269
Knock Knock
Who's there?
Lettuce.
Lettuce who?
Lett-uce in, it's cold outside.

270
Knock Knock
Who's there?
Witches.
Witches who?
Witches the way home?

271
Knock Knock
Who's there?
Tank.
Tank who?
You're welcome.

272
Knock Knock
Who's there?
Scott.
Scott who?
Scott nothing to do with you.

273
Knock Knock
Who's there?
Robin.
Robin who?
Robin you! So hand over your cash.

274
Knock Knock
Who's there?
Nanna.
Nanna who?
Nanna your business.

275
Knock Knock
Who's there?
Luke.
Luke who?
Luke through the peephole and you'll see.

276
Knock Knock
Who's there?
Boo.
Boo who?
What are you crying about?

277 Knock Knock
Who's there?
Justin.
Justin who?
Justin time for lunch.

278 Knock Knock
Who's there?
Nobel.
Nobel who?
No bell so I just knocked.

279 Knock Knock
Who's there?
Kenya.
Kenya who?
Kenya keep the noise down,
some of us are trying to sleep.

280 Knock Knock
Who's there?
German border patrol.
German border patrol who?
Ve vill ask ze questions.

281 Knock Knock
Who's there?
Ice cream!
Ice cream who?
Ice cream, you scream!

282 Knock Knock
Who's there?
Tish.
Tish who?
Bless you!

283 Knock Knock
Who's there?
Midas.
Midas who?
Midas well let me in.

284 Knock Knock
Who's there?
Arch!
Arch who?
Bless you!

285 Knock Knock
Who's there?
Howard.
Howard who?
Howard I know?

286 Knock Knock
Who's there?
Red!
Red who?
Knock Knock
Who's there?
Red!
Red who?
Knock Knock
Who's there?
Red!
Red who?
Knock Knock
Who's there?
Red!
Red who?
Knock Knock
Who's there?
Orange!
Orange who?
Orange you glad I didn't say red?

287 Knock Knock
Who's there?
Avenue.
Avenue who?
Avenue heard these jokes before?

288 Knock Knock
Who's there?
Debate!
Debate who?
Debate goes on de hook if you
want to catch de fish!

289
Knock Knock
Who's there?
William.
William who?
William mind your own business?

290
Knock Knock
Who's there?
M-2.
M-2 who?
M-2 tired to knock!

291
Knock Knock
Who's there?
Waiter
Waiter who?
Waiter minute while
I tie my shoe.

Left over right...
no...right over left...
...right behind the left one
left...

292
Knock Knock
Who's there?
Army.
Army who?
Army and you still friends?

293
Knock Knock
Who's there?
Wooden shoe.
Wooden shoe who?
Wooden shoe like to know.

294
Knock Knock
Who's there?
Who.
Who who?
What are you—an owl?

295
Knock Knock
Who's there?
House.
House who?
House it going?

296
Knock Knock
Who's there?
Icy.
Icy who?
I see your
underwear.

WOW!
These things
REALLY DO WORK!
I can see
UNDERWEAR!!

UNDERWEAR
FUNCTION
X-RAY
BINOCULARS

297
Knock Knock
Who's there?
Alaska.
Alaska who?
Alaska one more time . . . let me in!

298
Knock Knock
Who's there?
Butcher.
Butcher who?
Butcher little arms around me!

299
Knock Knock
Who's there?
Stopwatch.
Stopwatch who?
Stopwatch you're doing and
open this door!

300
Knock Knock
Who's there?
Canoe.
Canoe who?
Canoe come out to play?

Why did the boy throw butter out the window?
Because he wanted to see a butterfly!

 What's black when clean and white when dirty?
A blackboard.

302 What has eyes that can not see, a tongue that can not taste, and a soul that can not die?
A shoe.

306 Why do firemen wear red braces?
To keep their trousers up.

303 What is there more of the less you see?
Darkness.

307 What kind of dress can never be worn?
Your address.

308 What word is always spelled incorrectly?
Incorrectly.

309 What has a bottom at the top?
A leg.

310 What's an ig?
An Inuit's house without a toilet!

304 How many apples can you put in an empty box?
One. After that it's not empty anymore.

311 What's the last thing you take off before bed?
Your feet off the floor.

312 What goes up and does not come down?
Your age!

313 How many seconds are there in a year?
12 . . . 2nd of January, 2nd of February . . . !

314 What runs across the floor without legs?
Water.

315 What has holes and holds water?
A sponge.

316 What kind of ship never sinks?
Friendship!

317 What has four fingers and a thumb but is not a hand?
A glove!

318 What belongs to you but is used more by other people?
Your name.

319 Where were potatoes first found?
In the ground.

320 What bet can never be won?
The alphabet.

321 What is the beginning of eternity, the end of time, the beginning of every ending?
The letter 'E'.

322 What can't walk but can run?
A river.

323 Why did the golfer wear two sets of pants?
In case he got a hole in one.

324 What does every winner lose in a race?
Their breath.

325 What has 22 legs and two wings but can't fly?
A soccer team.

326 What illness do martial artists get?
Kung flu.

327 When is a baby like a basketball player?
When he dribbles.

328 What did one bowling ball say to the other?
Don't stop me, I'm on a roll.

329 Why were the arrows nervous?
Because they were all in a quiver.

330 What do you get when you cross a footballer with a gorilla?
I don't know but nobody tries to stop it from scoring.

331 Why do soccer players have so much trouble eating?
They think they can't use their hands.

332 Why are baseball players always so cool?
Because of all the fans.

333 Why was the chickens' soccer match a bad idea?
Because there were too many fowls.

334 Why is tennis such a noisy game?
Because everyone raises a racket.

335 Why is Cinderella so bad at sport?
Because she has a pumpkin for a coach and she runs away from the ball.

336 What is the smelliest sport?
Ping pong!

337 Why did the runner wear rippled sole shoes?
To give the ants a fifty-fifty chance.

338 What's a ghost's favorite position in soccer?
Ghoul-keeper.

339 Why did all the bowling pins go down?
Because they were on strike.

340 Why was the centipede two hours late for the soccer match?
It took him two hours to put his shoes on.

341 Where do old bowling balls end up?
In the gutter!